An Essential Guide for any Parent with a Child in Sports

#HeySportsParents!

Sharkie Zartman and Dr. Robert Weil

Published by Spoilers Press, Hermosa Beach, California

ISBN: 978-0-9992510-4-1 (print)
ISBN: 978-0-9992510-5-8 (ebook)

Book Design: Deana Riddle, Founder of BookStarter
Cartoons: Damian Fulton, President of Dream House Productions

Photo Credits:
Universal Event Photography: *Dancer Emma Johnson*
Jerry F. Pillarelli: *Chrissie Zartman soars into her jump serve*
Daniel Ikonomi: *Alex Budina, the soccer player*
Nancy Ryan: *Chloe Ryan on the ice*
Carson Smith
Shutterstock

"My mother made me strong. She never let me blame anyone but myself for failure. She never let me feel sorry for myself. She did not allow excuses. She did not allow me to bask in my glory when I won. She didn't accept anything from me but my best. She taught me to work for what I want. I can't thank her enough!"

– Evan Lysacek and his mother Tanya - 2010 Figure Skating Olympic Gold Medalist

"I first put orthotics in Evan's skates when he was 10 years old. The rest is history. It was a highlight of my career and quite a ride!"

– Dr. Bob

Contents

Welcome to the wacky, challenging, up and down world of youth sports!

Dr. Robert Weil and I are excited that you picked up #HeySportsParents and hope to give you the essential tools and guidance to make your experience as a sports parent the best that it can be. Dr. Bob and I have over seventy years of combined youth sports experience, I, myself, as a former All-American volleyball athlete, sports parent, youth and college coach, and Dr. Bob, a sports podiatrist, who has treated and worked with elite top level young athletes for decades.

The book is divided into four sections. The first section, *Sports Parenting 101*, includes eight chapters on the necessary survival skills of parenting a young athlete. I have put together all of my best tips and advice in this section to help you understand the territory of youth sports. Topics include the benefits of youth sports, the pitfalls and risks, how to find the best program for your child, parental roles and responsibilities, parental coaching, nutrition, how to help your child through the college recruiting process, and stress management for parents.

The second section, *The Sports Doctor is IN*, has valuable insights and advice from a doctor's perspective. Dr. Weil, an accomplished sports podiatrist, has worked with hundreds of young top-level athletes and their parents for over forty years. Take his advice to heart to keep your child healthy and hopefully free of injury. He will cover how to keep your child safe, youth sports and drugs, choosing the best shoes for your athlete, orthotics, prodigy sports, and the genuine risks of contact sports for kids.

In the third section, *The Experts Speak Out*, we have assembled some of the best minds in sports parenting to share their insights. First, Robert Andrews, the owner of the Institute of Sports Parenting, shares the Power Triangle; Kate Davis, a registered dietician, explains how to create a solid nutritional fueling plan at a young age, and Dr. Denise McDermott shares the connection of youth athletes and mind medicine. Then, Dr. Holly Benjamin and Dr. Claire Gross share their advice for parents on youth concussions and sports; Ian Goldberg, the creator of Isport360, discusses the behavior of overzealous sports parents on the sidelines, and Dr. Dave Epperson, the founder of the Volleyball Festival, gives us the seven habits of savvy sports parenting. Lastly, Melissa Orth Fray shares how you can help your child become a better athlete; Janis B. Meredith shares what great sports parents DO, and Dr. Steve Horwitz from www.team-safesports.com talks about youth sports safety on the field.

In the last section, *Parent Perspectives*, we highlight different sports parents as they describe their journey with their children. Their insights and suggestions will make you realize that you are not alone; whatever you experience is not unusual, but likely to be very common among parents. The challenges and sacrifices made for a child to make it to the top level of a sport are tremendous for both the athlete and the parents. Our contributors include Kirk Mango, Cat

Dols, Nancy Ryan and Timmer Halligan. Trust me. Not only are their stories inspirational but there is also a lot of excellent advice for parents.

We hope that your sports journey with your child is a positive one, but also know that it will be filled with ups and downs. The hardest part of sports parenting is watching our kids play the sport and not having any control over the outcome. Being a supportive bystander while trying to navigate the terrain of choices is a totally different experience in parenting. However, if done correctly it can be most rewarding. So hang on, and get ready for a wild, unpredictable ride! Here we GO!

Sharkie Zartman
Follow us on twitter! #HeySportsParents

Section One

SPORTS PARENTING 101 WITH SHARKIE ZARTMAN

You know that being a parent is challenging, but you probably feel that you've got it down to a science by now. After all, you survived sleepless nights, countless diaper changes, the terrible two's, have raised your child from a helpless baby to a young person that you kept safe from the imminent harm of just moving around, and endured the separation anxiety of dropping him or her off at daycare or preschool. The hardest part of parenting is behind you. Right?

Not necessarily.

Trust me, being a sports parent is both a unique and challenging experience.

Up until now, you have called all the shots and have done almost everything that you can for your child to keep him or her safe, happy and healthy. But once your youngster starts to play sports, you have to become an observer as you watch your son or daughter go through the ups and downs of being an athlete. At times it is elating and wonderful. Other times, it can be stressful and painful.

Here's a relevant quote from Earl Wilson, a former professional baseball player and columnist: "For the parents of a Little Leaguer, a baseball game is simply a nervous breakdown into innings."

No one really can understand what is going on until they experience it for themselves. Being in the stands or the bleachers while your child is playing a sport sometimes makes you feel as if an invisible outside force is overtaking you.

Watching your child hit a home run or score a winning goal or basket is enough to send you into a crazed frenzy of celebration, while the opposite is true if your child is taken out of a game, chastised in front of others, or messed up a play and the team lost as a result. I have seen the calmest people display aggressive behaviors toward coaches, athletes, or referees, and others transition into crying babies at youth sporting events.

You also never know how inappropriate you can be until someone criticizes your child or what an obnoxious jerk you can become if your youngster is one of the stronger performers. Sports by their nature have the potential to bring out both the best in us and the worst.

So where do you learn how to be a great sports parent so that your child can be successful and you don't end up having a nervous breakdown?

Welcome to #HeySportsParents!

Chapter 1
The Real Values of Playing Sports

I was so excited when my daughters told me they wanted to play volleyball. I was still competing at the professional level, and my husband was training many of the top beach players in the country. With all the volleyball going on around them, my daughters had the opportunity to experience the sport up close and personal and were ready to dive in.

As a result, we created a beach training program for kids made up of a group of our daughters' friends and family members. It was meant to be fun, but also emphasized footwork and techniques they would need to have if they ever wanted to pursue the sport later.

Well, that time came sooner rather than later as the kids kept persisting in their desire to play against other teams. We checked out the volleyball clubs in the area, and none of them were taking athletes under eleven years old. So my husband and I started our own junior club, and never looked back.

Our club team had the youngest kids in the tournaments, and not only did they have efficient skills, but they taught everyone in the gym one of the most important perks of playing sports — having FUN! At every tournament, they were excited to get on the court, and hear their parents cheer for them.

However, the first game they won was confusing for the kids because even though the parents were cheering wildly, the game stopped. One of my young athletes looked at me bewildered and said, "Why did we have to stop playing coach?" I said, "Because you won! The game is over." She seemed disappointed because she just wanted to keep playing. Winning didn't mean that much to her. That was an eye-opener for me.

My journey with sports as an athlete, coach, and parent taught me a lot of lessons that had a significant impact on my life and I believe they are the real reasons why sports are so valuable for our children.

1. **The Accountability Factor.** The first lesson is the most important. Being responsible for the choices we make in life is empowering. Unfortunately, kids who never have any accountability for their choices and actions will continue through life thinking nothing is their fault, and everything is owed to them. However, in sports, no one else can play for them, including the coach and the parents, so eventually, they do learn that what they do, or don't do, does matter.

   Most athletes know that if they blame others for their losses, they will never get any better. Imagine what our world would be like if everyone held themselves accountable for their actions instead of projecting and blaming others. Sports is a perfect training ground to develop this important life skill.

2. **Making mistakes is necessary to learn how to do things right.** Remember when your child started walking for the first time? Did he or she just stand up and walk perfectly? I doubt it. There was probably a lot of wobbling and falling before it became second nature. It was a process and so is learning how to play a sport. As parents and coaches, we need to help our kids get through the learning process and not expect them to be great from the start. If kids are afraid of making mistakes, they will be hesitant to try anything new and might develop a fear of failure. Participating in sports is a great way to teach our children that learning something new usually takes time and if they want to be successful, they need to be patient.

3. **Athletes know that they don't get to win all the time.** In fact, a loss is when athletes are the most motivated to make essential changes.

Generally speaking, when athletes get knocked down, they typically don't stay down, whine, and complain. They get back up and are usually stronger than before. Most athletes are tough and love the challenges their sport brings. Ultimately, they end up using this resilience to handle life's challenges.

4. **Athletes can take criticism.** Obviously, in every sport, there is a coach who is responsible for getting the best out of his or her athletes. Sometimes, that means being very honest about their weaknesses. An athlete has to be able to handle the truth…a trait that makes most people uncomfortable but is necessary if a person wants to be successful.

5. **Persistence equals success.** Athletes spend hours trying to perfect their skills in practice, so they have the best chance of success. Those hours pay off in the long run. The old saying, "practice makes perfect" might not be 100% accurate, but practice certainly helps people succeed. What's incredible is that many people give up on their dreams too soon. Unfortunately, we tend to live in a "the quick fix" society. We don't want to wait for anything. In sports, kids learn that sometimes they need to be patient and keep trying. There is usually another opportunity to succeed because there is always another game, tournament or season down the road. As long as they are working on improving and trying their best, success will ultimately become attainable.

My husband was known for telling our athletes not to focus on winning, but to focus on doing their best every time they stepped on to the volleyball court. If they did that, they would be successful, and the winning would eventually take care of itself.

6. **Athletes learn that they must follow the rules.** All sports have rules and also consequences if the rules are not followed. Our kids need to be in situations where they must follow the rules so they will be

law-abiding citizens when they grow up. I'm sure you have seen both kids and adults who think the rules don't apply to them and have felt frustration with their total disregard for the laws and other people. Sports teach kids that they must follow the rules of the game, or both they and their teams will be penalized. A great lesson!

7. **Sports teach kids that sometimes life is not fair.** As parents, we know that intuitively, but usually protect our kids from experiencing this reality. However, in sports, there will always be times when the referees make bad calls, when one athlete plays more than others and doesn't deserve to, or a team loses even though they tried their best.

8. **Athletes learn to respect themselves, their coaches and their teammates.** In a me-me world, being an athlete is an excellent way for kids to learn to respect not only themselves but also their fellow athletes and coaches. There are several athletes and coaches that I competed both with and against over the years that taught me a lot about focus, resiliency, competitiveness, and many other life skills.

9. **Playing a sport is a great way to exercise and have fun at the same time.** Unfortunately, with all of the cool technology available these days, most kids are not getting the physical exercise they need to be healthy. Combining fitness with a sport is an excellent opportunity for kids to enjoy working out and also get the essential benefits of physical activity.

10. **Last, but not least, is teamwork.** Being on a sports team is one of the best opportunities to learn how to get along with other people and hone communication skills. Both are of utmost importance in any job or relationship. With most of our kids using cells phones and social media to communicate, many are losing the critical opportunities of

actually talking to other people face to face and understanding body language.

In sports, you don't have to like your teammates, but you must learn to work with them for the team to be successful. Besides, it always feels great when your team wins a hard-fought contest, especially after putting in long hours of practice together. Often these teammates can become life-long friends.

After years of playing sports and coaching at the high school, college and club levels, I believe that these lessons are the real perks of playing sports. However, as a society, we focus too much on the wins, championships, trophies, and the opportunities for scholarships which are all just icing on the cake. Even if a kid eventually does get a college scholarship or plays professionally, at some point, he will most likely have to earn a living doing something else. No one can be a career athlete forever.

As parents, grandparents, and coaches, we need to keep our focus on what is important — *how our kids can be more successful in life by playing sports.* The lessons are there for the taking.

I DID KICK OUT THE ROWDY PARENTS. THOSE ARE THE **GRANDPARENTS**.

So if your child or grandchild is playing a sport, realize that there are going to be good times, and also challenging times. You cannot control the winning or losing. But you can support them along the way, and make sure they are in situations where these lessons are valued.

Recently I picked up my three-year-old grandson, Calvin, from pre-school, who was visibly upset because his soccer group lost to the blue team. So I asked him a couple of questions:

"Calvin — did you have fun?" He smiled and said yes.

"Did you try your best?" He smiled again and said yes.

"Well, then don't be upset. Remember that you can't do any better than your best, and it's just a game."

Then I took him to Mulligans, a family fun center, to let him ride the cars, play video games and air hockey. He was having a great time until we got to air hockey, because, as usual, I beat him. However, this time he was closer to winning than ever and immediately demanded to play one more game. I have never seen him so determined as he furrowed his eyes, glared at me and was breathing so loud he was nearly snarling.

Then he proceeded to beat me 600 to 400. Trust me. I tried to win.

After the game, I said, "Oh my gosh Calvin, you beat me!" He gave me a little smile and then these words came out of his mouth: "ZMA, did you have fun?" (He calls me ZMA) "Yes," I sheepishly said.

Then he asked: "Did you try your best?" I smiled and said yes. (I really did try to beat him.)

And then he ended with: "Remember that you can't do any better than your best and it's only a game. So don't be upset."

Then he flashed a HUGE GRIN!

I guess I learned my own lesson. (Although it was a little humiliating losing to a three-year-old.)

Finally, remember that the number one reason why kids play sports is that they are fun! Why would any kid want to play a sport that isn't fun? It's not their job and should not be perceived as a chore. So as a parent, make sure it is fun for them and also you.

Chapter 2
The Pitfalls and Cautions of Youth Sports

Yes, playing sports as a youngster has a lot of benefits and the lessons learned can be transferred to challenges later on in life. However, sports can also be a minefield that can be damaging to a child and it is every parent's responsibility to be aware of the negative influences and risks that sports might present. Too often, we as parents, tend to focus on the winning and excitement of being a part of a sport, and sometimes don't notice when our child might not be benefitting and is at risk of being hurt not only physically, but also emotionally.

Here are some common pitfalls.

1. **How much does it cost?**

   We all want what is best for our children, but when it comes to playing sports, you don't always get your money's worth. Many clubs charge huge fees, and parents are drawn toward these "elite clubs" that make it sound like every child will be a champion and earn a college scholarship. We have several of these volleyball clubs in our area, and I get many phone calls from disgruntled parents who complain about paying over $5,000 a year, usually up front, for a club, where their child never gets to play or is on a horrible team with an equally horrible coach.

   Paying a fortune for a club sometimes places undue pressure on a child. He or she might start feeling that the sport is a burden of responsibility rather than an outlet for fun.

So before you sign your child up for one of these expensive programs, do your research. Talk to parents who are in the club, or better yet, parents who *were in the club and took their child out*.

One of the parents who called me said that a club guaranteed that his son would play in college if he joined. But during the season, his kid played sparingly, got little coaching of value, and was unhappy. However, he was a member of a successful team that won a lot of titles. The dad said that if he could do it again, he would not have put his son in that club. Instead, he would have chosen another program that was less expensive where his son would have had a better opportunity to play. In doing so, he would have saved enough money to pay for his son's tuition at most colleges. So buyer beware.

2. Commitment Challenges

When you sign your child up for a sport make sure you can get your youngster to the practices and games before you join the program. This could be your child's first lesson in commitment, and you are the one who will be a significant part of it. I see too often parents signing their kids up for teams, but then are flaky about showing up. Obviously, if the kid is sick or there is a family emergency, those reasons are valid. But if a child learns that he or she can decide when to attend or when not to, it is not fair to his teammates and the coach. Also, the child has missed out on a valuable opportunity to learn how to commit to something and be accountable for showing up. And we all know that commitment and accountability are life skills necessary for success in both our relationships and careers.

3. Safety Issues

No parent wants to see his child get injured playing sports. However, injuries do happen, and all we can do as a parent is to make sure precautions are taken to reduce the risk. So make sure your child has the best equipment that will minimize the risk of injuries. Having proper footwear, orthotics, knee pads, ankle braces, and a helmet if necessary are essential. Make sure that your child's team has safety as a priority. Too often, some coaches and administrators are more focused on winning championships than keeping your child safe.

One of the most dangerous safety concerns in youth, college and professional sports is the risk of concussions especially in contact sports such as football and hockey. Also, soccer is being targeted, especially for younger athletes because of heading. Research indicates that a young person's neck is not strong enough to withstand the force of a substantial impact to the head. As a result, many experts are now recommending neck exercises as part of the conditioning to make the neck stronger to sustain any contact that may occur.

Also, there have been many innovations recently in the design of helmets for football, skating, biking and other sports as well. However, there is still considerable concern about contact sports and concussion risk. This will be discussed in more detail later in Dr. Weil's Section, and also in the Experts Speak Out Section with Dr. Holly Benjamin and Dr. Claire Gross.

4. Your Child's Coach

Your child's coach is a major variable as to whether or not your child will have a positive experience. Not only must the coach understand the game and be able to teach fundamentals, but he or she must also be able to efficiently communicate with the kids and parents, and also be a good role model. Most people who coach kids do so because they love the game and want to help kids. And coaches have very different personalities, with some being rather quiet and serious, and others being loud, fun and playful. However, there are some "Svengali Coaches" who end up being too obsessed with winning at all costs, and can be emotionally and physically abusive to their athletes.

One of my friends was ecstatic when her daughter made a high-performance club, in which the coach had won several national titles. He apparently knew the game well, but was verbally and physically abusive to his athletes: calling them names, grabbing and pushing them if they didn't win and using foul language.

After witnessing these behaviors, the mother realized that winning was not more important than her daughter's emotional health and took her out of the club. Thank goodness! And besides, what was this coach teaching his young female athletes? That this was the way women are treated?

When it comes to choosing a coach for your child, make sure he or she not only understands how to coach the game and get the best out of the athletes but also treats the athletes with respect and never puts them in uncomfortable situations or abuses them in any way. Demeaning or insulting a young child by a coach is never acceptable and should not be tolerated by parents.

The bottom line — choose your coach carefully and make sure he or she is a good fit for your child.

5. Overtraining

This is a huge concern, especially with high-performance clubs. Some of these young kids are being subjected to three-hour practices four times a week while playing in tournaments on the weekends. Others, not only do the required workouts with their teams but also get personal coaching for both conditioning and techniques. Remember that young kids are growing, so if their bodies don't get rest, they will get not only be sore but also often put themselves at risk for chronic injuries. Also, some kids play more than one club sport, and that usually doubles the risk. Too much is too much!

6. Specializing Too Soon

I see this a lot in sports, when a kid is assigned a position on a team at a very young age, and then just keeps working on being the best that he or she can be at that position. What if it is not the best fit?

For example in our volleyball club, we had no idea as to how their young bodies were going to develop, so we made sure that we taught the athletes all the skills and how to play all the positions. This philosophy worked out well for our athletes because they were valuable to their high school teams since they were so adaptable.

Congratulations! It's a middle blocker!

CARTOON BY DAMIAN

Also, be careful of having a young child specialize in only one sport. Let them try different sports as long as they are not too time-consuming. If they really start to like one sport and want to be the best they can be in it, then, and only then, should they specialize.

For example, I thought my younger daughter had the potential to be a great gymnast, and she did exceptionally well when she was young. But the physical and time demands were too much as she got older and she eventually quit because she also wanted to try soccer and volleyball.

At the time, the commitment for both sports was less time than she was expected to spend at gymnastics. It worked out great for her. She eventually fell in love with volleyball, played in both high school and college and was named a Division 1 NCAA All-American at UCLA.

7. Burnout

Sometimes, we don't see this until it's too late. Kids usually won't complain about playing a sport because they feel that their parents are having so much fun watching them play. Often, kids start playing a sport and love it, but might outgrow it or have other interests.

I once had an athlete who was a great setter and was so happy to make our team. However, towards the middle of the season, I could see that she was unhappy and finally pulled her aside and asked why she was playing volleyball. She honestly told me, that she was doing it for her dad, who was her #1 Best Fan. She said that while she liked the sport, she didn't love it, but she loved her dad, and that's why she was playing.

Obviously, this was not a good situation for her, and she confided that she really wanted to get into art but was afraid to tell her dad. To make a long story short, she eventually worked up the courage to confide in her dad about her wishes and did not continue with the club the next year, even though she was one of our best players. However, I was so proud of her for being honest, and we did replace her with another fantastic athlete who was incredibly motivated!

Also, watch out for kids who get so obsessed with a sport that the rest of their lives are dysfunctional. Obviously, this is the opposite of not being motivated, but it can have detrimental effects because kids, like us, need to have balance in their lives. So make sure they have friends, other interests, and they are doing well in school. Sports should not take over their lives.

8. Winning at Any Cost

Trust me! I loved to win and always prepared as an athlete and coach to do just that. However, losses do occur, and sometimes they can provide the biggest lessons along with the motivation to work harder.

So, make sure that your young athlete, is not only motivated to win, but is also able to take losing in stride, and use it as an opportunity to improve. If as a parent, all we care about is winning, then a child will feel undue pressure to win. This can have disastrous effects such as feeling that he let his parents down, not wanting to play anymore, or developing a fear of competition.

I know one parent who used to take his kid for ice cream after his team won. But he never took him to get ice cream when the team lost. This kid was eight years old, and the next year, decided he wanted to quit because he couldn't stand to lose. SAD.

9. Mental Challenges and Stress

Stress is usually defined as the way we respond to change. There are going to be a lot of changes going on when your child is playing sports, so not only will your child be exposed to stress, but so will you! Remember, that playing a sport should ultimately be fun for a kid, but also should provide challenges for him or her to grow and that sometimes is not easy. It is a roller coaster of emotions, both positive and negative.

But realize that being able to manage stress is a huge advantage for children as they get older. We need to make sure that our youngsters are efficiently learning how to deal with challenges and stressors, and also not have them see us overreact when something goes wrong.

Make sure you really listen to what your kids are telling you about their experiences playing sports, and neither trivialize nor dramatize their messages. The last chapter in this section talks more about stress and how you can manage it as a sports parent.

10. Over-Parenting

I know that watching your kids play a sport at times is hard, but we must realize that when they are on the field or the court, it is THEIR experience.

HEY MOM! HEY DAD! IT'S NOT YOUR GAME!

When it comes to communicating with the coaches, eventually children should be taught to communicate and advocate for themselves. This will show self-reliance, a lifelong skill that will help children as they grow to learn that mommy and daddy are not always going to take care of everything. Trust me, coaches want to have happy athletes on their team, but would prefer to talk to their athletes about any issues they may have instead of the parents, especially as the kids get older.

As parents, we tend to make excuses for kids to shield them from stress. In sports, that is a No-No. Excuses don't allow for improvement, and in sports, the athletes are usually trying to improve on all levels. As we know, we can't control winning or losing, but we can control how we handle challenges, and sports have a way of throwing a lot of curve balls. So, stay grounded and watch your child grow and learn while playing a sport that he or she enjoys. Don't get in the way!

11. **Sexual Abuse in Youth Sports**

As you are probably aware, sexual abuse in youth sports is a reality as evidenced by the accusations of athletes from both the USA Women's Gymnastics Team and the USA Swim Team. Over 160 female athletes were sexually abused by the Team USA's Doctor in gymnastics, and over 590 athletes have reported sexual abuse or misconduct by their swim coaches and trainers when they were under eighteen years of age. This has been going on for decades.

Unfortunately, both organizations were supposedly aware of these incidents for years and did nothing about it.

Why? Because of their image, reputation, and financial interests.

But now, we are finally seeing a turn in the tide. The USA Swimming organization is under investigation for having several coaches who have abused underage athletes over the years and several board members have been removed from their positions. USA Volleyball and the Amateur Athletic Association just banned one of the top club volleyball coaches in the country who has repeatedly been accused of having sexual relationships with his underage athletes. And the USA Women's Gymnastics team doctor was sentenced to 40 to 175 years for sexual assault.

Hopefully, all sports organizations will finally wake up and prevent these assaults from happening in the future. We need to have background checks, a formal code of conduct, a zero- tolerance policy for sexual misconduct and severe consequences for these transgressions all of which must be strictly monitored and enforced. It's unconscionable to think that these young athletes were subjected to these types of abuse and nothing was done to protect them.

No coach, trainer or anyone associated with a sport's program ever has the right to harass or abuse an athlete sexually. This should NEVER be tolerated by a parent. While most of the abuse occurs at the top levels in sports, there is still a concern at the beginning levels, and parents need to be able to make informed decisions about the well-being of their children. No parent would knowingly subject their child to that type of abuse in exchange for a championship or medal.

While most schools and recreational programs require background checks before they hire their staff, club sports usually do not require any screening or background checks when they hire their coaches. Obviously, this HAS TO CHANGE because a youth sports program would be a perfect place for a pedophile to coach young athletes and gain their trust.

So how can you prevent this from happening to your child?

Always ask if a club or organization does background checks on their coaches and staff and if they have a policy in place addressing harassment and abuse. If not, ask that they implement one, immediately. Too often, clubs focus mainly on a coach's ability to win medals and championships as a requirement for hiring.

As parents, our children's emotional, mental and physical safety should always come first. That's why we need to be proactive. Don't automatically assume that boys are not also sexually abused. Sometimes the targets of abuse are boys of single mothers who are looking for a father figure for their sons.

Private one on one coaching is very prevalent these days, and most of the time is a great way for young athletes to learn how to execute the skills of the game more efficiently since they are getting personalized attention. However, avoid dropping your child off and coming to get him or her after the session. (unless you know the coach very well.) Even though most coaches are trustworthy, you would certainly not want to put your child in a dangerous situation.

Here are some warning signs that parents need to be aware of that could indicate a real cause for concern.

When a coach or staff member of the club or organization:

- Spends one-on-one time with children without a parent present or offers to drive a kid in his car alone.

- Starts to give a child special attention or gifts.

- Touches a child in a way not related to training for the sport.

- Tells sexual or inappropriate jokes and stories to children.

Establishing an open line of communication with your children is vital in protecting them from predators. Make sure you let your sons and daughters know that they can come to you with any problems or concerns that they might have and you will listen, support, and still love them no matter what they say. The earlier you can establish this safe communication with your children, the better.

Also, make sure they know the proper names for their body parts. I know this sounds odd, but children need to know this information. Make it clear that your children are aware that no one is allowed to touch their genitalia unless it is a doctor doing an exam and a parent is present.

So when it comes to preventing sexual abuse, parents need to be vigilant, do research, and make sure they have established an open line of communication with their children. In the case of younger children, a parent should also stay for practice and be there for the games.

Hopefully, in the future, with screening and policies in place for all youth sports organizations, our children will no longer be at risk of being a victim of sexual abuse while participating in a sport.

Chapter 3
Finding the Best Program for Your Child

When it comes to playing sports, the commonalities that most kids share are that they want to participate and have fun. However, most children also have other goals and expectations, and that is where, we as parents, need to match the program to our child's desires and needs.

Keep in mind that your child is not a mini-me. Just because you were a successful athlete and a fierce competitor, or just love sports does not mean that he or she will follow suit. So taking an honest look at your child is the first place to start when deciding what sport's program would be best for your son or daughter. We need to match the program with our child, and also be ready to change when and if our child changes.

Besides height, body type and quickness, we need to consider our child's unique personality. Certain children seem like born competitors, and others seem more passive and agreeable. If you put your child into a program where the coach is always stressing scoring and winning, the passive child will not want to play. This is especially a problem when the parent is a competitor, and the child is more easy going and just wants to hang out with other kids and play nice.

Also remember that it takes a while for a child to learn a new skill, and many sports have a lot of techniques they must master before becoming proficient. So be patient! Hopefully, you will have a coach for your child who teaches the techniques correctly and allows the athlete to make mistakes while learning.

A common question that comes up with parents is "At what age can my child start to play a sport?" That is really up to the child. When they start mimicking the game or ask you to play it with them is a good start.

When a child is ready *to learn* a game is another matter. A child will usually be able to perform a variety of motor skills by the age of four or five, but the combination of tracking, rebounding and developing agility takes longer.

GEORGE'S REVOLUTIONARY "YOU'RE NEVER TOO YOUNG FOR FUNDAMENTALS"
THEORY IS ABOUT TO BE SERIOUSLY CHALLENGED.

When you combine this with a relatively short attention span, you can see why teaching kids at this young age is difficult. A good rule of thumb is to introduce skills when they are ready to learn them with the emphasis on fun and trying to do the skills correctly.

There are generally three stages most kids go through when considering interest and motivation for participating in a sport. The ages are approximate as not all kids are alike in progression.

Stage One: Ages Four Through Eight

In this beginning stage, children are most interested in having fun. They do love to win, but the fun factor is why they are playing in the first place. You can find playing opportunities at recreational programs such as AYSO, Little League, and local YMCA's. Some kids might be ready for clubs and travel teams, but don't get them into these too soon unless you know they have a strong self-esteem, are ready to handle losing, can handle both criticism and sitting out on occasion, and long time commitments.

Stage Two: Ages Nine Through Twelve

As children get older, some of them get more competitive. They want to get a shiny trophy or a sparkling medal. When they first get one of these trinkets, they usually will be motivated to get more. Sports still must be fun, but they are usually willing to spend more time practicing and will be more open to coaching and how to do the skills correctly if it will help them be more successful.

I remember one mother who was thrilled because her daughter's soccer coach said that their only goal for the year was to have fun and that everyone would have equal playing time. She was pleased to hear this because she thought her daughter would be happy in this situation, and not experience any stress. The coach was true to his word and played everyone equally and emphasized fun. (a recreational program) However, the team lost most of the games. To the mother's astonishment, her daughter was devastated.

I told the mom that perhaps her child was turning into a competitor, and was willing to give up a little fun and work harder to have more success. As children cross this line, they begin to realize life's rewards do not come easily. That is what competition is all about. Some kids cross this line early, others later, and some never. Remember, not all kids need to be competitors in sports, and they should never be forced across this line by a parent. Unfortunately, this happens far too often. Children who do not cross into competition should still be able to enjoy sports at the recreational level for enjoyment and to keep fit.

We hear stories all the time about kids who were forced into competition before they were ready and now hate sports and as a result, avoid physical activity because they had such a bad experience when they were young. In fact, seven out of every ten children who play sports end up quitting before they are fourteen. Sometimes they just lose interest, but most of the time, it's because they didn't like the pressure and the way they were treated by the adults who so desperately wanted them to win.

Stage Three: Thirteen Through Eighteen

In the final years of childhood, we see many athletes who are not as concerned about winning as they are with achieving their personal best. Even though they still love to win and get honors and awards, personal peak performance is more important. But even at this stage, playing sports still needs to be fun, and most athletes will put in more time and effort to reach their optimal goals.

The Program Menu

The number one mistake a lot of parents make is assuming that all sport programs are similar. Nothing can be further from the truth. The purpose of each program must be clearly defined and understood by the parent, child and the coach for everyone to support each other, and have the best experience.

Recreational Programs

The meaning of the word recreate means to *give new life to*. For a child, this means *to play*. Long before adult-organized recreation kids were recreating on their own. They created games with their own rules and played for hours on end. However, in today's world, most of the sports for kids are controlled by adults.

In adult-organized recreation programs for kids, the emphasis should be on participation and fun. *"Everyone plays"* is always a clue that the program is recreational. The emphasis in this type of program is on movement and partic-ipation. The skills of the game are taught, but teaching is not the primary goal of a purely recreational program. The participants learn by doing and enjoy the sport at its most fundamental level.

Instructional Programs

An instructional program is where skill progressions and techniques are taught. The participants also learn the rules and strategy of the game. Some kids do not like these programs because they just want to play. School physical education classes, private and group training, and clinics are examples of these programs.

Make sure your child is mature enough for an instructional program and can follow instructions, wait in line, and be respectfully attentive when the instructor is teaching.

Competitive Programs

Any program that has tryouts and makes cuts is a competitive program. To compete, athletes must earn playing time. I always recommend that kids do not enter a competitive program until they have strong self-esteem, have developed the necessary skills needed to compete, and both the kids and parents are aware of the nature of competitive sports.

Coaches in these programs have different criteria for why where and when they play athletes. Their goal is to make the team successful. However, the highest quality coaches also aim to get the best out of each athlete.

A purely competitive program usually does not involve a lot of instruction. It is assumed the players already have the skills and are able to help a team be successful. Young kids are sometimes not prepared for a purely competitive situation because they still need a lot of work on the basics. Also, some kids are not ready to earn a position and don't want to sit on the bench. These kids would be happier staying in a recreational program.

Hybrid Programs

As you can see from these program descriptions, there needs to be some overlap to have programs for all kids. Most youth programs are combination (hybrid) programs that are either instructional-recreational or instructional-competitive.

Adding the instructional component to either the recreational program or the competitive program naturally provides more learning opportunities and helps the kids become more successful at a sport.

Instructional-Recreational Programs

This program combines learning and playing together. The amount of time spent doing each depends on the age and maturity level of the kids. When children are very young, a more considerable amount of time is spent on playing the game, with a lesser amount spent on learning. The reason is that children usually have short or variable attention spans especially before the age of seven. As children get older, they can listen longer, and are often more interested in learning how to do things correctly so they can win!

The keys to a successful recreational program are to teach the skills and techniques correctly and maximize participation. The best programs and coaches turn skills into games instead of drills and emphasize fun.

Instructional-Competitive Programs

A combination program of instruction and competition is the gold standard for an athlete who wants to be successful. Most games are won and lost at the fundamental level — in other words, the team that makes the most mistakes loses. We have seen many kids thrown into a competitive sport without first refining their skills. Obviously, this is very frustrating for a parent to watch. Even at the professional level, most athletes will tell you that they are constantly refining and practicing their skills.

Beware of the competitive program that just splits up the team and has the athletes compete against each other. While this does have value, it is also essential to review skills and give the athletes feedback. As a parent, make your expectations clear if you want your child to have coaches focus on improving and refining skills, especially since most of these competitive programs (clubs) can be very expensive.

Recreational Versus Competitive

Recreational and competitive programs are in direct opposition to one another. Even though they both focus on winning to some degree, in recreational programs, everyone plays, and the emphasis again is on participation and fun. In competitive programs, the players usually must try out, earn playing time and a position and try to make the team successful. Big difference!

I know one coach who told the players and parents that the kids were all going to play in his program and have fun. After collecting five hundred dollars for each child, he changed his mind and turned it into a competitive program when he decided his team might have a shot at winning a title. He benched half of the kids, started pressuring his team to win and berated them whenever they made a mistake. Naturally, and understandably, many of the parents were upset. And no, they did not win the title that he was so desperately seeking.

Problems always arise when a child is in the wrong program. Remember that ideally, sports programs for the youngest kids should be recreational and instructional. The transition to a competitive situation should be the athlete's choice, not the parents'. Some kids will never want to be in competitive sports, but they should still have the opportunity to play. We need both recreational and competitive programs for kids, but they should be distinct from each other. Otherwise, there will be kids who are either left out, unhappy or stressed out, and parents and coaches in conflict.

Chapter 4
What is Your Role as a Parent When It Comes to Youth Sports?

This is a tough question to answer because it really does depend on the coach and the program. But I can give you a little perspective by having you answer this question:

If *you* were coaching a youth team, what kind of parents would you appreciate? What would you want them to do to help the team? And more importantly, what would you NOT want them to do?

Another question is to step back in time and imagine that you are the kid that is playing the sport. What would you want your parents to do to help the team, and again, more importantly, what would you NOT want them to do?

When my husband and I coached club volleyball, we had three simple rules for the parents.

1. Cheer for your kid and good plays from both teams.
2. Get your kids to the games and practices on time.
3. Let us do the coaching.

We also let them bring food to the tournaments, and that worked out well since they were all willing to bring healthy food and drinks for the team to share. They even brought a portable table with a tablecloth. Now that was classy!

We did have some problems at times with parents asking about why some athletes played certain positions and some played more than others, but we always were honest about the athletes' abilities and told the parents if they weren't happy with the situation, they were free to leave the club at the end of the season.

We did not give the parents any administrative duties and instead tried to make their contributions simple and easy to implement. It seemed to work for us as coaches, and our athletes won four national titles.

Remember that there are a lot of different programs and coaches, so what worked for us might not work for others. Maybe a coach or a program would appreciate having a parent do some of the administrative work, or be an assistant coach, or volunteer to referee a game if needed. But as I mentioned before, each situation is different, and if you sign your child up for a youth sport, you will have to make sure you understand and abide by program and coaches' guidelines for your child's sake. Be sure to ask the coach what his or her expectations are for the parents. Don't wait until there is a problem.

One thing is for sure. Never give your child's coach unsolicited advice. I don't care how much you know about the sport or how little the coach knows. Just ZIP it! If the coach needs your advice, he or she will ask for it.

I know what it feels like to watch your child play a sport and not be able to help. Even though we coached our children in club volleyball, they played other sports and also had other volleyball coaches at their schools. While most of the coaches were good with our daughters, sometimes our minds ran amok during the games with thoughts such as:

> "If they would only do this they would win."
> "Why is the coach taking Lisa out of the game?"
> "That was the stupidest play I've ever seen."

I know that we can't control our thoughts all of the time, especially when adrenaline fuels them, but we can always control our actions. Even that is hard at times.

Even though all parents are different, some behaviors are commonly exhibited at youth sporting events by parents. Remember that we all love our kids and want them to succeed, but not having any control over what happens once the game starts can sometimes trigger bizarre responses.

Some parents are a bundle of nerves. They can't stay still during the game and usually pace up and down the outside of the court or field. Nail-biting, hair pulling, and other psychomotor tensions are very noticeable. By the end of the game, they are either still breathing hard or slumped over in exhaustion and are usually sweatier than the athletes. Thank goodness most teams don't compete every day. These parents need time to recover before the next competition.

Others tend to feel everything they think their child does during the game. They might make motions with their bodies similar to what their child is doing on the court or field. Sometimes, they will just move their head or arms, but some parents get into it with their legs too. They are very alert as to what is going on during every play. I remember one woman was so focused on her daughter during a volleyball match that she wasn't even aware of other people or her surroundings. If you tried to talk to her, she would act as though you weren't even there.

I have also seen parents acting as if they were playing the game on the sidelines wearing a jersey similar to their child's.

I'm not kidding.

Too bad the coach can't substitute this parent into the game because he is warmed up and ready to go!

I have also seen some parents who are the most docile, quiet people I know jumping up and down and screaming at the top of their lungs when their child is playing a sport. Sometimes this is appropriate if it is positive cheering, although it can be embarrassing for the athlete. However, it is definitely **not** appropriate if the parent is booing or yelling at the team, the coach, or officials.

So be ready for anything! You might really surprise yourself while attending your child's game. Remember that your kids will probably notice any of your extreme behaviors and might be embarrassed. Imagine how you would want your parent to behave if it were you out there playing the game as a child.

One thing is for sure. Kids do not feel good about themselves if the coach is telling them one thing and the parent is telling them something else. There needs to be a feeling of unity and understanding for the child to succeed. *The coach and parents need to be on the same page for the child to be successful and enjoy playing sports.*

So your roles and responsibilities as a parent are quite minimal when it comes to the games. However, as a parent, there is a lot you can do to help make playing a sport a positive experience. That happens both at home and on the ride home after a game.

When driving your child home from an event, it is always fun when the team wins, and your child played great.

But what if the team lost or your child didn't play or made critical mistakes that contributed to the loss? What is your role then?

Most times, kids don't want to talk about the loss and would rather be left alone especially on the ride home. However, parents typically will try to make the child feel better by blaming the loss on the coach, the other kids, conditions, or the officials.

This might make the child feel a little better, but it is the wrong coping technique. The child learns to make excuses and doesn't learn to take accountability for his actions. Obviously, when kids are still young and just learning the game, they should be told by their parents that everyone makes mistakes and that making mistakes is sometimes necessary to get better.

Always focus on what your child did do right and his or her effort. When I was young, my dad always asked me whenever I felt bad about losing if I tried my best. If I could honestly say yes, then it made me feel so much better. As my dad always said, "You can't do any better than your best."

Also, don't treat your child differently when he wins or loses. Remember your job as a parent is to give unconditional love. I have seen some kids punished by their parents if they didn't play well in a game. Do you think the child is going to want to play again? Probably NOT.

So don't just give them ice cream when they win. Sometimes, after a loss, it is much more appreciated since ice cream always makes everyone feel better!

Empowering Your Child to Communicate with the Coach

Another area where you can help your child tremendously is to encourage him or her to feel comfortable enough to communicate with the coach about playing time or what they can do to get better, or any other concern. This can start at a young age.

Most coaches appreciate and encourage their athletes to communicate and would prefer talking to their athletes about any problems instead of hearing it come from their parents. You can obviously BE there when your child is talking to the coach, but let your kid do the talking.

It will be a tremendous gift that you give to your child to encourage this kind of communication because it empowers them to resolve problems instead of relying on others to do it. If the coach becomes abusive or doesn't allow the child to talk, then obviously you should step in and voice your concerns.

Model Being a Good Sport

This is so important because it teaches your child to have CLASS. You can't just tell your child to be a good sport, you have to be an example. You already know as a parent that what you do is more important than what you say. So be careful about your behaviors when your child wins a game and also when he loses. We have all seen parents exhibit extreme behaviors of getting way too excited about winning a game and also way, way, way, too upset about a loss. Remember, that a sporting event is just a game and nothing more.

Teach Your Child to Be a Good Teammate

Another valuable lesson parents can teach their kids while they are playing a sport is that it's not all about them! It's about helping the team win and accepting other members of the team without prejudice or judgment. Too often, kids don't get the experience of playing with others outside of their social circle, race or religion. Sports are great opportunities for youngsters to come together and work for a common goal. So make sure that you are supportive of not only the other kids on the team but also the other families.

Finally, make sure your child is having fun playing the sport. Remember that it is NOT their job. For some kids, there is a potential to play in college, professionally or in the Olympics but the chances are very slim. Less than 2% of the kids playing youth sports will get a Division 1 college scholarship and only one out of every 3,000 college athletes will ever play professionally.

When children are young, they should want to go to the games and practices, and not dread them. Your ultimate role as parents when your children are playing sports is to make sure they are learning, growing and also enjoying the experience. If you can do that, it will hopefully be fun for you too!

Chapter 5
How to Coach Your Own Kid

Coaching your child in a sport can be a fantastic bonding opportunity, a lot of fun, and fulfilling — but TREAD CAREFULLY. It could also destroy your relationship with your kid.

Coaching your son or daughter is a wonderful opportunity to spend more quality time with your child. Many parent-coaches have played sports before and want to be able to share their expertise with their child and the other kids. I guarantee that you will have lots of memories both you and your child will cherish for many years to come if you follow some simple guidelines.

We know that a lot of parents become youth coaches because they want to help and usually end up starting out as volunteer coaches. Most recently, one of my daughter's friends, Larissa, volunteered to coach her son's AYSO soccer team even though she had two kids and a full-time job. She volunteered because she wanted to help. No one else would do it and if there weren't enough coaches, the season was going to be canceled.

It was fun, but also demanding because the kids were only four and five years old and most of them didn't know anything about the game. She did an incredible job and worked tirelessly…all for free. But it was a special time with her son and his teammates and a positive experience for the kids. I watched all of the games since my grandson was on the team. What a wonderful first sporting experience for these young boys!

Way to go coach!

While most parents' intentions for coaching are noble and well- meaning, even the best coaches and parents can run into problems when their son or daughter is on the team. If you are considering coaching your child, the most important thing you need to know it that this will probably change your relationship with your child. The coach-athlete relationship is a special one and also a stressful one. There are likely to be great times interspersed with some tough times. Make sure you are ready to handle both.

I wish that all parent coaching experiences could be positive and stress-free, but unless you also know the challenges and some of the pitfalls, you could be in for a huge disappointment. Sometimes parenting and coaching do not mix well.

So here are some things you need to know.

As a coach, YOU are the one who will be making decisions about who plays where, why, and how often. That will directly affect the athletes on the team (your kid's friends), their parents, (sometimes your friends) and your child. Also, your son or daughter may become a target on the team for others' displaced aggression. Are you ready for this?

My husband and I started a volleyball club for our daughters when they were young because they wanted to play but were not old enough to be in a club. We never imagined that we would be coaching our daughters until they went off to college, but that is what we did. In the process, we learned a lot about the dynamics and challenges of taking on the responsibility of coaching their teams.

If you are thinking of coaching your son or daughter, even for a short period, we want to share some guidelines, insights, and tips. These will hopefully make your job easier and the experience more positive for you, your child, the other athletes on the team, and their parents.

Insights and Guidelines

Hopefully, you will have parents who are appreciative and supportive of your coaching. The chance of you having great parents are directly related to your communication skills, your goals, and your ability to treat your kid objectively and their kids fairly.

Some parents become resentful and negative toward a coach for many reasons. Most of the time this disdain stems from the belief that their children are not treated fairly and the coach's child is getting preferential attention. This becomes obvious if:

- Your child never gets any criticism, and their children do.

- Your child is always the star and their children never get any praise.

- Their children split playing time, but your kid is always in the game even if he is not playing well.

Another way to understand parents is to imagine yourself in a situation where your son or daughter is not getting a fair chance because of a coach who is favoring his kid. How would that make YOU feel? Make sure you don't become the coach you would hate if the tables were turned.

Parents will sometimes voice their concerns to you, but most of the time, they will harbor them inside, and make themselves and their child miserable.

One of the ways to circumvent parent problems is to first look at your child objectively. This may be the first time you have ever done this, but when you coach children, you are trying to teach them, not just the sport, but how to work for what they want. If they don't have to work at anything when they play for you, then they are not going to learn anything.

Remember, never use your coaching as an opportunity to showcase your child. It will be a temptation at first because you might be able to get away with it at least initially. But if you love your kid and want this sports experience to be the very best it can be for him — do not play favorites. In fact, sometimes being a little tougher on your child can help him be more accepted and respected by his teammates and their parents.

The other athletes on the team might also use your child as a target for their displaced aggression if they are not getting enough playing time or feel picked on. They might not show you their discontent, but they most likely will let your son or daughter know what they think. Your child might feel stuck in the middle because either he doesn't want to tell on his teammates, or doesn't want to tell you because it might hurt your feelings. Make sure you keep the lines of communication open with your athletes and parents, and especially with your child.

Also, if you are married, you need to make sure you and your spouse are on the same page as to how you are coaching your child. Otherwise, you could be in big trouble because you live with this parent. Talk about being in the dog house!

So coaching your child's team could be the hardest job you ever love, and also sometimes hate. Here are some tips to make it a mostly positive experience for everyone.

Tips

1. Talk to your child about what your role as a coach means. Make sure he or she knows that it is different from being a parent.

2. Listen to what your child's reasons are for playing. If he just wants to have fun and be with his friends, hopefully, the team you are coaching is mostly recreational. If your child wants to be as good as he can be and wants to be on a winning team, then hopefully the team you are coaching is mostly competitive.

3. Avoid living through your child. Just because you were a great athlete, or wanted to be, doesn't necessarily mean your he or she wants to be like you. Also, conversely, if your child is a great athlete, there is no way you can become one through him or her.

4. Let your child know he will be treated just like every other child. That includes discipline and skill corrections. Remind him that you are the coach when you are with the team, and that is your job. However, being a coach will never diminish how much you love your child. Make sure he knows that.

5. Have a meeting at the start of the season for all the parents and kids where you outline your goals and expectations for the season. Be as caring and professional as possible. Let the parents know that you are there to help all the kids and also make the team successful. If you need any help, let the parents know what they can and cannot do. Many coaches could use help with managing responsibilities and also appreciate parents bringing food to the games for the team. Don't be afraid to ask. Most parents do want to help, but sometimes will instead end up giving you unsolicited advice.

6. Do not bring problems home. Leave them in the gym or on the field. Remember that your child lives with you, so do not give him double

duty when there are hard times, like losing a close game. Also, never blame another kid or a referee to justify a loss.

7. Find a person who can help you keep a fair perspective. This person should be as objective as possible. (Probably NOT your spouse) Usually, other coaches can offer a good support system for each other, especially if they are also coaching THEIR child's team.

8. Learn as much as you can about your sport. Take seminars, read books, and get as much information as you can about how to coach at your level. This will not only help your team and increase your credibility, but it will also boost your child's confidence in you.

9. Make sure you spend extra time with your child away from the coaching when you can just be Mom or Dad. Trust me. This is important!

10. There might be times when your kid tunes you out during a game and doesn't seem motivated by anything you say. Let's face it — we are not always the person our child will listen to in every situation. I know one successful baseball coach who has his manager do most of the motivating chatter and coaching to his son during the games, while the coach motivates the manager's son. For them, it works great and might be a technique to consider.

The Golden Rule

Treating other kids as you treat your child is the Golden Rule for coaching a team with your child on it. If you adhere to this philosophy, everyone concerned has the best chance at success and happiness, including you.

Chapter 6
Nutrition is YOUR Responsibility; Learn How to Feed a Young Athlete Properly.

I remember hearing a story about a mother who had taken her ten- year- old son to the doctor because she thought he had a brain tumor. His symptoms? He was eating all the time and was always hungry! The doctor examined him, but before he ordered any tests, he asked what the boy was eating. The mother recited a litany of processed and fast foods — chips, cupcakes, donuts, cereal, cookies, French fries, hot dogs and so on.

Thankfully, the doctor realized that the boy was not getting the nutrients he needed for his growing bones and muscles, and that was why he was so hungry. His brain was counting the nutrients, not the calories, and kept sending a strong message for the boy to eat MORE! The doctor told the mother to add fresh fruits, vegetables, whole grains and clean proteins to his diet — in other words — to crowd out the junk foods. The boy started eating less and within eight months, grew four inches.

What's interesting is that healthy nutrition is not hard to understand, but in our society, it's hard to accomplish because of all the unhealthy choices that surround our kids and us. I'll bet you can't go for two miles in a populated city without seeing at least one fast food restaurant.

When you walk into a grocery store, take a look at all the processed foods that are full of sugar and chemicals. Many of these products are marketed to children with pictures of familiar characters or animals that they recognize, and are also placed on shelves at children's eye level.

As a parent, one of our most significant responsibilities is to feed our children foods that will fuel their bodies, help them grow, and also keep them as healthy as possible. As a sports parent, you are even more responsible since your son or daughter's body will be challenged with physical activities and will need the energy to play the sport, and require proper nutrients to recover. Children usually trust that their parents know what is healthy for them. It is a parent's responsibility to teach their children proper nutritional habits.

Also, as parents, we are role models, so if we eat healthy foods, we teach our kids to do the same. Unfortunately, the opposite is also true: If we eat poorly, so will our kids. Having your child play sports and being mindful of his nutritional habits could also help you, the parent, eat better.

Obviously, this is a lifestyle, but you can also help your children be more successful in their sport if you make sure they eat properly before a practice or a game. Here are some foods to stay away from before:

1. Sugary foods and drinks will elevate blood glucose, which will set off an insulin reaction in the body. Usually, in thirty minutes, the blood sugar level will drop causing fatigue. Obviously, you don't want kids to be tired right when they need to have the most energy.

2. Carbonated drinks can cause gastrointestinal distress. Their stomach will hurt because of gas. Also, if there is caffeine in the drink, it might cause dehydration, which can be serious if the weather is hot.

3. High protein and fatty foods will stay in the stomach for an extended period of time and cause discomfort and lethargy if they are eaten too close to game time or a practice.

So What Should Kids Eat Before Practice or a Game?

Two or three hours before a game or practice they should have foods high in complex carbohydrates. These would include whole grain bread, cereals, pasta, vegetables, and fruit. A little bit of protein can be added which would include light meats like turkey and chicken. However, don't have them eat foods with a lot of fat since it will most likely stay in their stomachs and make them feel heavy and lethargic. They should never practice or compete if they haven't had anything to eat at all.

On the days of tournaments, parents can be a big help to the team and coach if they come together and bring healthy foods for the athletes to have on hand during the day. Our club parents shined when we had all day volleyball tournaments. We even had one woman who brought portable tables with tablecloths, napkins, plates, and cups. Parents were each assigned to bring one healthy item to share with the team, and I have to say, our kids ate well and never ran out of energy. We were usually in the finals, and part of the reason was because our kids were so well fueled!

Here was the list of items parents typically brought to all the tournaments:

1. An assortment of fresh fruits

2. Vegetables and hummus dips

3. Nuts, bagels, nut butter and jams (be careful though with peanut butter since some kids might have severe allergies to peanuts)

4. Whole grain bread and light lunch meats

5. Small ready to eat sandwiches

6. Homemade cookies (Okay, you have to live a little ☺)

7. Whole grain crackers

8. Greek yogurt and natural granola

9. Water

10. Ice

11. Muffins

As a coach, the healthy snacks were greatly appreciated and it was a wonderful team bonding experience. We were always thankful that our parents went above and beyond the call of duty when it came to feeding our athletes. The food was always healthy and delicious.

Remember that one of the most essential nutrients your child needs to have on hand when playing or practicing a sport is WATER! Make sure your child always has access to water, before, during and after the practice or game. Not only can dehydration interfere with your child's performance, but it can also be dangerous.

If you can teach your children that foods with sugar and chemicals will not help them perform well at their sport, you will be giving them a tremendous gift that might affect how they eat for the rest of their lives. Also, make sure they realize that their bodies have to have the proper fuel not only to play the sport well, but also to feel good and stay healthy.

For more information on Fueling a Young Athlete, check out Creating a Solid Fueling Plan at a Young Age written by Kate Davis in the *Experts Speak Out* section. She is the owner of RDKate Sports Nutrition, a national consulting practice that serves athletes as young as eight and up. In her article, she gives sports parents excellent advice as to what works with young athletes, and also what doesn't work.

Chapter 7
The College Recruiting Game
What Parents Need to Know NOW

The first time a child starts a sport, many parents already have *visions of college scholarships dancing in their heads*. While this may be a realistic goal for some kids, it should never be the main reason why a child participates in a sport.

Yes, I know that getting your child's college expenses paid for either partially or fully is a big deal, but the recruiting process is a tedious experience for both the athletes and the parents. Think of it as a two-year interview process where one slip-up could prove costly.

Also, to some parents, landing any scholarship at any cost seems to be more important than the college degree itself. There is a reason why colleges use the term, *student-athletes*. They are students first, and athletes second. While it would be great to brag to your friends that your child got a scholarship to a college, the most important thing to consider, for your child's sake, is whether or not it is a good fit for him or her.

Keep in mind that the colleges are not only evaluating the athletes during the recruiting process. They are also evaluating the parents. So while you are watching your child play a game or match, if you scream at the coach or the officials, the other team, or your kid, remember you could be sitting next to a college recruiter. So be on your best behavior for your child's sake.

Remember that there is a fine line between helping your child through the recruiting process or becoming overbearing and even interfering with your child's chance of being recruited. In fact, a former recruiting coordinator for a Division 1 college once said: "It isn't unusual to drop a prospect from the recruiting board because the parents are a problem." OUCH!

So how can you help?

There are some important things you can do from the beginning of your child's sports experience. For example, besides coaches looking for athleticism, talent, skills, and sometimes body type, they also look for qualities such as attitude, communication skills, ethics, effort, good grades, and teamwork. These are skills you can start teaching your children, NOW.

We have an epidemic of overprotective parents who tend to do everything for their children. While being protective is part of being a parent, remember that sports, by their nature, put our kids in situations that we cannot control. The field or the court is a great training ground for teaching life skills, and as a parent, we sometimes just have to watch and support our kids. For some parents this is a first time experience.

I know. It's hard.

Once my daughter was on an elementary school softball team, and the pitcher got hurt, and they didn't have a back-up. No one wanted to try pitching, that is, no one except my daughter, who had never done it before.

Seeing her walk up to mound I started to feel panicky and sick to my stomach. I almost gasped. "Is Teri pitching?"

She looked so confident, but from the first pitch, I realized that everyone around was in danger of being hit by a wild pitch. People were running for cover when the ball left her hand. It was painful watching, but we just kept cheering as the other team walked around the bases. Eventually, the game was called because her team had gotten "skunked."

We laugh about it now, but at the time, it was grueling. I was praying the coach would take her out, and let someone else try. But at the same time, I was so proud of her persistence!

I know that sports are challenging for kids, and also for their parents. But our role is to be their cheerleaders and support system. At no time should we tell our children how bad the coach is, or how incompetent the refs are, or say anything unkind about their teammates. We need to zip it!

As mentioned in an earlier chapter, one of the best things we can do from an early age is to teach our kids how to communicate with their coaches.

Even if your kid is shy and nervous to talk to a coach, the coach would much rather hear from the athlete than the parent. And when it comes to college recruiting, this is imperative. After all, who is going to play for the coach for the next four years? Remember that the coach is recruiting your child, NOT YOU!

Most parents think that college recruiting does not happen until the start of the junior year in high school, but that's not true. That is usually the time when coaches can make contact with the athlete depending on the sport or the division. But coaches and scouts can go to any of the games and are watching athletes at younger ages all the time. I knew one dad who told me that his son, who played baseball, had been observed by college recruiters ever since he was nine years old. I thought he was delusional, but come to find out, it was true.

Once the recruiting process begins, parents should become the children's mentors and also their administrative assistants. In other words, they should NOT take charge. Parents are NOT responsible for marketing their kids. Remember that young athletes need to be the ones building relationships with coaches.

Here are some things you CAN and should do.

1. Remember that the most important goal is to get a good education. Discuss academic interests with your son or daughter and then check out the best schools that offer majors in those areas. Keep in mind that most kids do not go on and play professional sports out of college. In fact, the chances are approximately one in 3,000. Make sure your child realizes how important it is to get good grades in college, so he or she is prepared to enter the workforce after graduation.

2. Help your child make up a list of desired schools with some being "dream schools" and also some that are more realistic. Division 1 colleges only make up about 18% of all the colleges, so make sure you don't narrow your child's choices. There are many opportunities to play a college sport at Division 2, Division 3 and NAIA schools. Even though your child might want to stay close to home, realize that a student-athlete who is willing to go to a school away from home expands the opportunities.

3. As your child's administrative assistant, you can help organize your child's test scores and transcripts and assist your son or daughter in putting together an athletic-academic resume. You can also help by having your child write a letter to a coach at a college that he or she is interested in attending, and edit the letter. These duties are much more important and appreciated.

4. Many schools ask for a video of an unedited game or match. Hire a professional and make sure there is no music. (A lot of coaches hate the music!) Also, do not send a highlight tape. Coaches are not stupid.

5. Once your child starts filling out college applications, help them through the process but never do it for them.

6. You can also be a huge help by researching any financial opportunities, grants, work-study programs and scholarships that might help your child pay for college. Most athletic scholarships these days are not "full-rides." However, if you can get half of the tuition paid for with an athletic scholarship, there might be other financial opportunities that could help a lot.

7. Once your child has a list of desired schools, arrange a trip to visit the colleges. You can sometimes hit two or three on one trip. I have seen some student athletes set on going to one school change their minds once they walk around and see the campus. Also, try to take in a match or a game and watch the coach and the athletes. See if your child can imagine being out there. Sometimes, this can make or break a decision especially if there are evident problems with team dynamics or a coach is hot-tempered.

8. Check out as many resources as you can. The number one resource I recommend is: The NCAA Guide for College Athletes.

9. Be careful with your money. Youth sports can be very costly, and there are many camps and recruiting services that promise a lot. Realize that most college camps have a lot of attendees, and your son or daughter might get lost in the shuffle. Recruiting services are unregulated and can cost thousands of dollars with NO guarantee your child will get a scholarship just because you paid for the service. Most coaches don't need a recruiting service to let them know who the top athletes are. Remember, they have been watching for a long time.

10. There are now many showcase events where the event organizer invites college coaches to observe athletes go through a serious of drills and scrimmages to demonstrate their talents. These can be very expensive for the parents and do not guarantee that a child will even be noticed by a college recruiter because most of them are very crowded.

11. Realize that your child's high school or club coach is not responsible for getting your child a scholarship. They are trying to make the team as successful as possible. Also remember that if a parent is considered a nightmare by the high school or club coach, the chances are good that college coaches will find out. Coaches talk.

What Should You NOT Do?

1. Do not EVER email a college coach on behalf of your child. Also, never respond to a coach's email addressed to your child. This is a big RED FLAG to college coaches.

2. Never brag to a college coach about your child. It is his job to determine if your child is a good fit for the program. Remember, he has positions to fill, so even if your son is a great pitcher, the coach might have three others who are better at that position.

3. If you and your child are together with a college coach, DO NOT speak for your child. Be in the background. Let your child do the talking.

4. Do not decide for your child where he or she should go to college. Remember, it is your child's ultimate choice, and it probably will be his "job" for the next four years. A scholarship is not a free ride. The kids who do get scholarships work their butts off.

5. Never make a scene at an athletic event. Do not hurt your child's chances of playing in college just because you can't control your behavior.

Hopefully, you have learned a few things about how you can help, and not hurt your child's chances of playing in college. Remember that your child does not have to be on the best club or high school team to be seen by college recruiters. All they need is to have the opportunity to play on a team whose schedule puts them in front of as many college coaches and scouts as possible.

Remember that if your child is just starting out in sports, you, as a parent, have a lot of responsibility as to how your child behaves. Children learn from their parents so if you want your child to exhibit good sportsmanship, make sure your language and demeanor are first rate. Teach your young athlete humility, how to be a good team player and the virtues of a positive work ethic. I have seen many college coaches say no to a "star prospect" lacking these qualities. They would rather have someone who works well with the team and is a pleasure to coach.

Chapter 8
Stress Management for Sports Parents

I included this chapter because even if you think that you have your life in control and don't experience a lot of stress, you will need to have some stress management tools available if your child plays sports. Because *out goes your sense of control.*

Even though you do get to decide where your child plays, who the coach is, and how much money you spend, when it comes to playing time, positions, practice times, skill development, and referee decisions, you are on the OUTSIDE looking in.

Are you getting the picture?

So what can unmanaged stress do to you? Simply stated, it can make you sick, unhappy, and might cause you to act like a maniac. It can also damage your relationships, especially with your family and your child. Did I get your attention?

Okay, so what are some of the best stress management techniques you can use that will help immediately, especially when the fight or flight response hits you during a game?

1. Start taking deep breaths and count at least to four on both the inhale and exhale. This is best done with your mouth closed, just in case any inappropriate comments are about to make their way to your lips.

2. Remind yourself of at least one of these essential truths and say it over and over until it hits your brain.

It is only a game.

These are kids.

I can handle this.

The people officiating are human beings and sometimes make mistakes.

There are lessons in losing. No one wins all the time.

Damian

DON'T CRY DADDY, IT'S JUST A GAME.

3. After the game is over, physical stress relievers often help, and one of the best options is exercise. Every sports parent needs to do a physical activity if they are able. The intention is not necessarily to get in shape. The primary purpose is to dissipate the stress response. So if you haven't worked out for a while, make it a priority. The cool thing is that it doesn't matter what the activity is, as long as it is physical. I know of one woman who used to schedule her boxing classes right after her son's baseball games. It helped her for sure! You should have seen how hard she hit that punching bag!

4. If you have an unhealthy diet, now is a good time to clean it up. Your body and brain need to have nutrients, not toxins, to get you through the season. Make sure you are drinking enough water and cut down on the caffeine, which makes you more susceptible to stress. Watch your alcohol intake. Many people use alcohol as a stress reliever, so just be aware. If you notice you are drinking more than usual, cut back. You don't want to end up being a full-blown alcoholic at the end of your kid's season.

5. Also, spending quality time both alone and with loved ones is imperative. You probably have other stressors in your life besides being a sports parent so balance out the stressful times with those that are healing, soothing, and enjoyable. Another priority is to make sure you spend time away from the sport with your child, so he/she can see you at your loving best. This one is mandatory!!

6. Schedule get-a-ways or vacations where you can be in different environments. If you can't get away, try meditation. Or take a walk along the beach or in a beautiful area. In other words, get out of your normal environment.

7. Get a massage. It will help to eliminate the muscular tension that will be building up during the season. If you have never tried yoga before, give it a go. There are many different types so you should be able to find one that you enjoy. And one of the top benefits of yoga is stress relief!

Finally, realize, that stress comes with sports. There's no getting around it. However, it can be managed by having the right perspective, attitude, and also a toolbox of stress relievers.

Remember:

It's only a game,

These are kids,

And you CAN handle this.

Summary

As you can see, youth sports are fun for kids, promote health and fitness, teach sportsmanship, teamwork, accountability, and many other qualities. They are the perfect training ground for our kids to learn how to handle the challenges of life.

However, we have all seen instances where youth sports turn out to be an ordeal for both the kids and their parents and hopefully, this will NOT be the case for you and your child.

I hope that you learned a few key things in this first section that will help you navigate the world of youth sports, enjoy your experience as a sports parent, and also feel good about the prospect of strengthening your relationship with your son or daughter. These are experiences you will remember forever.

In closing this first section, as you travel the journey of sports parenting, I challenge you to notice how you interact with your child when he or she is playing sports. Is there camaraderie? Do you feel closer and more bonded because of your participation? If so, you probably have sports in perspective, and your child will reap the rewards of being an athlete.

Remember to make sure sports are fun for both your child and YOU. Always be there to support your child however you can without trying to take over. Remember, it is NOT YOUR game. It's your child's.

Next up, The Sports Doctor is IN! Dr. Bob Weil shares his insights and advice on parenting sports from a doctor's perspective. As a renowned sports podiatrist, he has treated many of the top young athletes in the country and will provide practical advice on how to make sure your son or daughter stays safe from injuries. He also shares ideas on proper training and a whole host of other topics. Take it away Dr. BOB!

Section Two

THE SPORTS DOCTOR IS IN

Hey Sports Parents! In this section, I'm going to share some important information about "the sports medicine" side of parenting the young athlete. In the late 1970s, I met Bob Gajda at Sports Fitness Institute in Glen Ellyn, Illinois. The SFI was way ahead of its time. Specializing in rehabilitation, sports performance, and training, the institute was one of the country's first Nautilus facilities. Specialists in orthopedics, chiropractic, personal training, nutrition, and massage were all involved.

Gajda was a Mr. America bodybuilding champion from the 60s who has since become one of the country's leading sports therapists. Athletes from around the world in all sports and at young ages came to consult with Bob for injury treatment, rehab and performance enhancement including members of the men's and women's Olympic volleyball teams. There were not only pros in all sports but also young adolescents in what I've since coined "The Prodigy Sports" — kids already specializing in a single sport such as gymnastics, figure skating, tennis, soccer, and volleyball. Of course, many sports parents came with their young athletes for consultations.

Specialization was nowhere near what it is today, but it was still a big deal. Multiple sports athletes along with many high schoolers were also in the mix. It was Bob's regard for the "role of the foot in sports" that got us together and still does. Philosophies and methods for strengthening the feet and ankles, working and improving balance, and the use of custom orthotics were all coordinated. Bob and I did numerous small-town radio shows back then talking about Chicago's Bears, Cubs, Sox, Bulls, Blackhawks and many of their athletes training at SFI. We also talked a lot then about concerns about injuries and overuse in young athletes and also about sports parents. That might have been the first time I thought about the book title: "Hey Sports Parents!" When we met the late Jim Vicory, a sport's psychologist, in the 1980s, "the mental game" really became part of the discussion on our radio shows.

In the early 1990s, I shared my radio show, "The Sports Doctor" with Jim Vicory for three years. WDCB, a great jazz, blues station at College of DuPage, Glen Ellyn, Illinois included some "specialty shows," and The Sports Doctor was one of them. Chris Fox, a local newspaper sports reporter, introduced and interacted with me for over fifteen years. Jim was a sports psychologist and sports trainer combined. We met in the early 1980s at Sports Performance and Rehabilitation Institute, the facility that replaced SFI. He worked on both the physical training side as well as the mental game. He called himself a performance enhancement consultant. He didn't use the term psychology because he believed that it gave the impression that something might be wrong.

Today, the terms psychology and sports psychology are used routinely. Jim was quite an addition to Bob Gajda at SPRI. We did many shows on the physical and mental challenges for both the kids as well as the parents. He had a few pearls of wisdom for sports parents such as:

1. Don't be a critic.

2. Give positive feedback.

3. Be a good listener.

4. Have a positive relationship and communication with coaches.

5. Insist on proper rest and recovery as well as proper training and nutrition.

These are all helpful tips for any sports parent.

There are seven topics that we will explore in the upcoming chapters in this section.

1. Keeping Your Child Safe, What You Need to Know About Preventing Injuries

2. The Challenges of Drugs and Youth Sports

3. Choosing the Best Shoes for Your Young Athlete

4. Foot Mechanics and Orthotics

5. The Prodigy Sports

6. Universal Exercises for All Sports

7. Hey Sports Parents — What About Youth Tackle Football?

Chapter 9
Keeping Your Child Safe
What You Need to Know About Preventing Injuries

Youth sports have always been popular for so many great reasons, and today is no different. Unfortunately, along with all the positive aspects of youth sports, there is also an alarming increase in injuries, especially overuse and repetitive motion injuries.

PREVENTION IS KEY!

Injuries happen in sports at all ages such as sprains, strains, broken bones, torn tendons and ligaments, and concussions. Many of these are acute injuries which occur suddenly during an activity.

However, the pressure to win, overzealous schedules, year-round participation, and specialization are all reasons why there is an increased incidence of sports injuries which are mostly attributed to overuse.

Some classic examples of overuse injuries are young baseball pitchers or swimmers with elbow and shoulder problems and running, jumping athletes with foot, ankle and knee concerns. These type of injuries are not the acute injuries that occur suddenly but instead tend to be chronic in nature. They are more gradual, more insidious, and often more difficult to identify.

"The terrible 2s" include doing too much, too often, too soon, too aggressively. They are examples of conditions that lead to overuse. Specialization in one sport is another concern with repetitive motion injuries at young ages. Using the same muscles, the same way for a particular sport contributes to overuse. Specialization sports, also called prodigy sports, focus exclusively on only one activity. Today most sports medicine doctors and therapists would argue that young athletes need to experience and play many sports as they grow.

Parents and coaches need to be keenly aware of these challenges and problems. They must listen and pay close attention to complaints from their young athletes. Relying on over the counter pain and anti-inflammatory medicine to continue participation is NEVER SMART! Making sure that persistent soreness or pain complaints are given proper attention IS SMART!

I tell parents all the time that using pain meds to "stay in the game" means you are over the line and you need to BACK OFF! Proper rest and recovery are essential in all sports at all ages.

Often, persistent and recurrent overuse problems and injuries, such as shin splints or knee problems, are related to body and foot mechanics that are associated with pronated or flat feet. Thus, it is important that your young athlete is evaluated by a sports physician or therapist if problems persist.

NEW NEWS:

The traditional ice-RICE protocol (rest, ice, compression, elevation), is under scrutiny as to its effectiveness in reducing swelling and stimulating healing.

Gary Reinl, who has worked with and trained many of the world's best athletes in all of the major sports as well as Olympic sports is the author of the book, *Iced-The Illusionary Treatment Option*.[1] The foreword is written by Dr. Gabe Mirkin, MD., who writes, "Almost 40 years ago I coined the term R.I.C.E. as the treatment for acute sports injuries. Subsequent research shows that rest and ice can actually delay recovery. Ice can help sometimes suppressing pain, but athletes are more interested in returning as quickly as possible to play. So today, R.I.C.E. is not the preferred treatment for an acute athletic injury."

Gary Reinl writes, "After 40 years of widespread use, there is no peer-reviewed indisputable published evidence that the use of ice improves the recovery process."[1]

So the question is:

What is the preferred treatment for the acute injuries according to Gary Reinl's research?

He calls it the "loading and muscle activation principles." Loading is also known as active recovery and is essential to achieving optimal healing of damaged tissue regardless of whether it just happened or it is an ongoing situation.

Muscle activation means stimulating the use of the surrounding muscles of an injured area. For example, if the injury is a sprained ankle and there is pain and swelling, then the muscle activation would focus on the movement of the toes and the muscles in the calf and knee area.

This technique stimulates blood flow through the injured area and helps remove waste products. This is more proactive than the ice-RICE method that inhibits recovery. Gary further points out: "Regardless as to whether you are sore, tired or injured the solution is always the same: achieve the largest amount of non-pain inducing muscle activation through slow controlled movement around the damaged tissue for as often and as long as is needed."

The idea is to initiate the cascade of events that work to protect the area from further damage, prevent or retard disuse atrophy, increase circulation, and, ultimately, heal the damaged tissue. Mostly, all that you have to do is "activate the system" since your body is already perfectly equipped to heal itself.

According to Reinl, "Always start with extremely minimal effort or movement and only move in pain-free natural planes of movement." For example, if the condition is in your foot, slightly wiggle your big toe by contracting and relaxing the involved muscles. Once that feels good you should do the same with your other toes again stimulating muscle activation to exchange fluids, reduce inflammation and activate the healing process.

If you are unable "to activate the muscles" in a specific area (for example, if you are wearing a cast) or it is just too painful to activate the specifically desired muscles or your doctor has instructed you to keep your damaged area immobilized, then you should still activate the muscles in the general area. For example, even if you cannot activate the muscles in your foot, you can still achieve good results by activating the muscles in your lower and upper leg.

Reinl recommends that the best time to begin the loading muscle activation process is as soon as possible. You really want to keep in mind that we are trying to activate the muscles without causing any pain or fatigue. You are not trying to strengthen muscles or do anything involved in the training situation. You are focused on recovery techniques, not training techniques.

Now, of course, all acute injuries ideally should be evaluated by a physician, therapist, or athletic trainer to determine the severity as well as the particular location of any specific injury that just occurred.

Chronic injuries are becoming epidemic in youth sports because of the pressures put on athletes to play despite injury or get back too soon after an injury. Many times a problem is preventable and short-term if we utilize intelligent rest, where you back off from the continued activity that is causing the problems, and then enter a proper rehabilitation program with a physical therapist, sports physician, podiatrist or other experts in sports medicine.

Overuse injuries are common in sports podiatry and often related to foot mechanics such as torque concerns of pronated feet affecting areas above like the knees. These tend to be more prevalent in young girls. Because of this we need to have sports physicals that include screening for foot mechanics, body type, range of motion flexibility and strength. All of these areas are great examples of evaluating who might be more susceptible to these overuse injuries.

Again, the repetitive motion injuries are similar to overuse injuries but result from specialization in sports where young boys and girls might be doing the same activity the same way using the same muscles repetitively. So parents need to be good listeners. They have to be aware and observe whether or not their son or daughter is complaining of pain. If so they should seek medical help.

It is not a good idea to take over the counter pain or anti-inflammatory medicine in order to keep participating. Even with the supervision of a doctor, these areas are still iffy. We don't want to live on medicine. Drugs in sports is one of the biggest problems we are facing today and it starts early where the young athlete might be taking some Ibuprofen before or after the sport it in order to keep the activity going due to pressures from parents, coaches, teammates, or themselves.

I highly recommend that parents who have a son or daughter specializing in only one sport work with a physical therapist or athletic trainer to work to develop a well-rounded strength training program to help prevent injuries relevant to that particular sport. Again, just playing the sport using the same muscles all the time is one of the problems. So regardless of whether your son or daughter is a dancer, a volleyball player, a figure skater, soccer player, or tennis player, the physical therapist can put them on a program that strengthens the total athlete, not just the muscles that are involved in the sport.

So again, we really want to reiterate some of the important points regarding various injuries in this chapter.

> #1. There is an epidemic of youth sports injuries from minor to severe, and the more serious your son or daughter is about his or her sport, the more we really have to pay attention to this.

#2. Quite often the injury is related to over scheduling and overdoing, or as I like to call it **overkill.** That's when sports can start to make these youngsters more susceptible to injuries, specifically overuse or repetitive motion injuries.

#3. The traditional R.I.C.E principals and the use of icing for acute injuries is not as helpful as originally believed (with the possible exception of numbing some initial pain,) and may actually be retarding the healing capability of the body. According to Reinl, a better option for athletes who want to return to their sports sooner would be loading and muscle activation. This is still big news and somewhat of a secret in sports medicine. Hopefully, we will see this change as more coaches, parents, trainers, doctors, and therapists become aware.

#4. The physical evaluation of young athletes in sports, as a rule is, somewhat limited. As a sports parent, you should include podiatry and a podiatrist who can help evaluate foot mechanics, foot type, and the best shoes for your athlete. These are all important. Orthotics can also play a major role in the prevention of problems and injuries related to balance and performance.

Also pay attention to:

1. Your child's age. Be aware of some sensible parameters such as too much jumping too early in figure skating, being on point too early in ballet, overloading schedules whatever the sport.

2. Your youngster's history of injuries and problems including muscle weakness, structural imbalances, and poor biomechanics. These are all examples of potential problems.

3. The level of competition. Be aware of not pushing your kids in "over their heads," especially too soon or too young.

You also want to be a good listener and be very aware of the kinds of pressures to which these young athletes are being subjected. These can lead to problems that might begin as quite minor but then become persistent nightmares simply because the parents, coaches or athletes themselves refuse to back off and pay attention to my two favorite words, "intelligent rest."

Chapter 10
The Challenge of Drugs and Youth Sports

The link between drugs and sports runs deep. Drugs and sports have been connected for about as long as sports have been played. This includes the whole array of painkillers and anti-inflammatory drugs both prescription and over the counter.

One of the concerns I've always had, especially at the elite and professional level, is that the physical and mental demands of sports all too often are extreme. This often leads to the using of pain meds and anti-inflammatory medication even in younger and younger athletes to survive. This "routine use" is alarming! The ibuprofens (Advil, Motrin), Naprosyn (Aleve), and aspirin are far overused to keep these young athletes "in the game."

NOT SMART! — Parents Beware! Youth sports injuries, both acute and chronic are at epidemic levels — we've got to pay real attention!

Are the schedules and physical demands we put on these kids often too much with not enough time for the body to recover? Too often the answer is yes! For the past three to four decades, I've watched as college and professional athletes and even Olympians faced these challenges. Now, not much is different at the high school level, and especially for adolescent standouts in club sports, particularly those who specialize in a single sport.

One of the difficult realities in the world of medicines and sports is that they work. Under proper medical supervision, medicine can be of real value. Problems arise when the drugs are used to replace proper rest and recovery. In past years, it soon became apparent to athletes, coaches, trainers, (and parents) that drugs work. This soon leads to rapid overuse and reliance on these drugs to shorten recovery time, dull pain and discomfort, and allow more intense workouts and training. BIG MISTAKE! We all know too well these endless stories at the highest level of sports.

This scenario, of course, has filtered down to young athletes. Prescription pain medications, like opioids, which are often given for sports injuries, have become a national epidemic nightmare. Seriously question your doctors if they prescribe these. It's not unusual to recommend over the counter anti-inflammation drugs for injuries in young athletes, but they should always be accompanied by strict guidelines and instructions for short-term use. This is always combined with decreasing intensity, frequency and level of training or playing, otherwise known as "intelligent rest."

An important rule for parents and coaches is that if they are using these medicines for their youngsters to participate or stay in the game, they have CROSSED THE LINE! I can't tell you how often I see this rule broken–especially when "the pressure to play is on."

We are bombarded with TV ads about all sorts of pain and anti-inflammatory over the counter medicines. It's easy for one to be fooled into thinking that all these drugs are without side effects or consequences and that is simply not true. Get educated! Besides the drugs themselves, the whole world of sports supplements and energy drinks are also of concern because children and adolescent bodies are still growing and developing. As a rule, most experts do not recommend these supplements under the age of eighteen. Again, the reality is that it's all too common for high school and even younger athletes to be using these easily obtainable products to try and "get an edge" over their teammates and rivals.

Parents should always check with their doctors or dieticians before allowing the use of any   sports drinks that contain high amounts of caffeine that can be potentially dangerous for some kids. Doctors have been alarmed that problems such as heart arrhythmias can be related to caffeine intake.

Let's not fool ourselves with this very important topic of drugs and youth sports. It's everywhere! Because youth sports injuries are of epidemic proportions, it stands to reason that all sorts of demands and problems are right there with them. Physical and mental pressures seem to be always increasing for our young athletes, so parents and coaches need to pay attention and listen and observe their young kids and players. Awareness and education are always the keys.

Chapter 11
Choosing the Best Shoes for Your Young Athlete

Paying attention to the choice of shoes and proper fit for young athletes is extremely important. There is no BEST shoe. Numerous brands and styles are available from which to choose. That's the point; there are lots of choices.

So let's talk about what's important:

1. Make sure you're choosing shoes that are designed for the sport. For the most part, it's smart to stick with what is designed with the sport's demands in mind. Good sturdy heel counters are important as well as the ball of foot flexibility, regardless of the sport. Only running shoes have different foot type criteria such as motion control and neutral or stability designs.

2. Stick with "name brands" with good quality. You don't need the highest price shoe. But stay away from bargain brands. If your young ath-

lete has had good success with a particular brand or style, stick with it. This is easier said than done because the brands are always changing. Hand me downs (wearing your older brother's or sister's shoes) is never a good idea. This can cause problems especially with running and jumping sports.

3. If your young athlete has foot, ankle, lower extremity injury history, or fitting problems, get a podiatrist's opinion. Some good questions to ask are: What is the best shoe for my son or daughter's foot type or mechanics? Might orthotics be beneficial?

4. In general, do not use running shoes for other sports. Running shoes are designed for straight ahead movement - not side to side field or court sports. You can use "cross trainers" for any of these multi-directional sports with few exceptions. They have good stability and motion control.

5. Cleats are traditionally used by soccer, baseball, softball and football players even at very young ages. The problem is that there are large growth centers in the heel susceptible to stress from running and jumping that can be aggravated by the cleats. Most heel pain in pre-teens is related to this. Get your youngsters into a multiple nub shoe that spread the pressure more evenly. These heel conditions called Sever's or apophysitis are quite common in soccer where heel cleats sit right under the growth center. The balls of the feet in growing children also have these growth centers, and again cleats can cause problems. I would like to see no cleats before adolescence, but it's a tough sell. If heel problems persist, get podiatry or medical evaluation. I've had great success with orthotics for these kids with chronic heel problems.

6. Proper fit is important! Would it surprise you to know that over 50% of all of us are not wearing the right size? That of course includes our young athletes, whose feet are still growing. Make sure that you go to reputable sports shoe stores with trained "shoe fitters." Make sure

both feet are measured for both length and width. Make sure shoes are comfortable. Sounds simple but if they don't feel great, don't buy them. A good idea is for the kids to wear shoes around the house for day or two to make sure they are really comfortable. If so, then play in them; if not, replace or exchange them. You don't want your young athlete to find out after wearing shoes for a practice or game that they're not comfortable.

7. Replacement of shoes is also important. Even if your child has not outgrown them, it is wise to replace sports or athletic shoes each season or at least twice a year due to wear and tear. Pay attention to the shoes breaking down. Look at the back of the shoes and check for heels rolling inward or outward. If cleats are used, check their wear pattern. If they are uneven, replace them.

8. Skates in both figure skating and hockey need special consideration. Proper fitting of boots in figure skating and hockey is crucial. I recommend only experienced boot fitters for both sports. Again, if foot problems develop, persist or recur, get a podiatrist's opinion because orthotics will probably be needed to alleviate the problem.

Chapter 12
Foot Mechanics and Orthotics

It's hard to believe that I have been prescribing custom orthotics for young athletes over the past forty years. Young boys and girls, from five-year-olds to teenagers in sports such as soccer, baseball, football, basketball, tennis, figure skating, hockey, running, and dance have all benefited from wearing proper orthotics for their sports. Athletes' concerns and challenges both physically and mentally are usually the same regardless of the sport. Quite often their overuse problems or discomfort is related to their foot type or mechanics. Almost always the reasons are persistent pain or discomfort, not an acute injury. Their feet, heels, shins or knees hurt especially with aggressive schedules and playing demands.

More and more, however, especially in figure skating, the use of orthotics has also improved balance, stability, edging, and performance. I have never had a skating coach or parent tell me: "The orthotics slowed my young skater down or they messed up their balance." Never!

Orthotics for growing kids might be changed every year and a half to two years. Once their foot growth is over, (girls about fourteen and boys about sixteen), they might use same orthotics for the next ten years. Rarely is larger shoe or skate boot needed for these inserts.

We'll get more specific with foot type, foot mechanics and joint position and alignment later this chapter.

Prescription in-shoe orthotics, properly done, ideally by podiatry, but also by well qualified physical therapists have really proven to be a major weapon in the treatment and prevention of foot related ankle, lower leg, knee, hip and back overuse problems.

The feet affect all areas above them from the ankles to the knees to the hips to the back in all of our lower body movements. Just like the song, *Dem Bones*: The foot bone's connected the ankle bone, the ankle bone's connected to the knee bone…all the way up the weight bearing chain. In running, jumping, skating sports- that's where it's at! So we have to realize how important it is to have healthy foot mechanics and support.

Orthotics are made from various materials. Often the demands and specifics of the sport can determine these materials. I have always liked flexible unbreakable polypropylene plastic for youth sport orthotics. Flexibility is determined by the athlete's weight and their sport.

Orthotics do much more than support the arch. They help properly position and align the foot, ankle, and lower extremity. Optimal joint position and structural integrity are the goals. Often the prescription is made using plaster cast molds of the feet in measured positions. These can be messy, but I believe they are the best method. Orthotics have various uses and indications. Examples are redistributing weight away from painful areas to control excessive or abnormal motion, or enhance alignment of the lower leg. Dissipating and reducing shock might be another important use.

A common misconception is that custom orthotics are arch supports. They are not. There are definitely uses and indications for over the counter inserts or supports, and often I'll recommend them for temporary initial use while we're waiting for the custom orthotics. But these are generic inserts by shoe size which do not have much effect on foot function or joint correction.

The main role of custom orthotics is usually to control the positioning of the feet and lower legs during the different phases of gait. Basically, the foot has three jobs in walking and running:

1. Shock absorption when the heel hits the ground.

2. Ground accommodation or shaping to the ground, (imagine walking on the sand).

3. Pushing off the foot like a spring lever.

Each of these actions demands particular motions of the foot and rotational motions of the lower and upper legs, pelvis and spine. The terms used to describe these foot motions are pronation and supination. These are complex motions taking place in the joints of the foot and the lower ankle — three motions in three directions simultaneously.

Only our hands are as complicated but we don't walk on our hands! I mentioned that once in a talk I was giving to young gymnasts and one of them said: " Yes we do."

Pronation (movement inward) and supination (movement outward) are normal motions of the foot. Problems can arise when the timing, velocity, or amounts of these motions are excessive or limited. Pushing off a loose hyper pronated foot is risky and can strain the supporting tendons and muscles.

Various inherited foot types and leg shapes create problems with these motions. Some examples are flat feet, high arches, bowed legs, knock knees and leg length differences. Each of these imbalances (quite common), can cause excessive pronation or supination leading to problems with overuse, wear and tear, arch, heel pain and knee pain and shin splints.

Foot type and leg shapes are commonly inherited. National health statistics and surveys show that over 75% of us exhibit some minor to major foot or leg imbalances. It's not surprising then with so many young athletes "pushing the envelope" that overuse and repetitive motion injuries have exploded around youth sports.

Foot Type and Mechanics

Many sports parents ask, " Does my son or daughter NEED orthotics"?

Better questions are:
"Would they benefit from them?"
"Will my young athlete be less susceptible to overuse injuries?"
"Will they help performance?"

Often the answer is yes to all the above questions!

Once sports parents understand that custom orthotics are designed to capture the optimum alignment and functioning position of the feet and lower legs, enhance the normal motion and position of the joints of the foot and ankle and that these devices are not crutches or arch supports, perhaps they will increasingly realize the importance of them.

Although not a cure-all, custom orthotics are a step up for both preventing overuse injuries and enhancing sports performance.

Chapter 13
The Prodigy Sports

We've mentioned prodigy sports in previous chapters. What do I mean by the prodigy sports? Specifically, I'm talking about sports that involve adolescents and younger who are specializing in only one sport. So often, young athletes and their parents are faced with the question regarding concentrating on their main sport versus playing multiple sports. Today it is not unusual to see kids younger than twelve, and some as young as six, already putting all their efforts and parents' money into one sport. The multiple sport athlete is far less common today than years ago. (Remember those lettermen's sweaters and jackets with letters for each sport?)

Some of the thinking by parents and coaches is that young athletes will fall behind if they play different sports instead of just one sport year round. This is a valid question with no exact answer. All experts agree that specialization is risky both physically and mentally. My bottom line has always taken into account the young athlete's passion and insistence on specializing. If your youngster says that he or she is not interested in other sports, you have to be aware of the concerns regarding specialization, especially in a very young child.

Here are some important factors regarding these prodigy sports kids:

Physically, with the young growing bodies, playing the same sport with the same movements, same muscles being used, with the same stresses to tissues, is a concern. Overuse injuries to the upper and lower extremities are a real problem. We've already noted that these injuries are a youth epidemic and many experts feel that specializing in one sport multiplies these problems.

It is essential to include off-sport conditioning that helps to develop the overall athlete and strengthen against these repetitive motion injuries. Concentrate on what Bob Gajda, a famous sports therapist called " strengthening the opposites and stabilizers." (The muscles and tendons that work against those repetitive motions). Athletic trainers, physical therapists, and personal trainers can help devise these programs. This kind or training is also helpful for multiple sport athletes.

Make sure that strengthening feet and ankles and working balance is always included regardless of the primary sport. The next chapter includes exercises that your youngster can do at home to keep these areas strong.

Tennis, figure skating, gymnastics, swimming, soccer, ballet, and volleyball are all examples of these prodigy sports. It's common for me to see young figure skaters under the age of ten already skating every day. They are not interested in other sports — period!

Most sports medicine doctors, physical therapists, and athletic trainers agree that playing multiple sports is a safer route to take where injuries are concerned. Almost all also agree that specialization is a greater risk especially for overuse and repetitive motion injuries. However, that is a tough sell for these prodigy sports. Too many coaches and traveling teams and club sports really push this idea that not specializing will cause these young athletes to "fall behind" in the contest to be the best for their sport. There is no evidence that this is true. There are many examples of great athletes who grew up playing a variety of sports who then after their teens specialized in one sport. I remember the vast majority of the women's Gold Cup soccer players said they played multiple sports growing up.

We've talked a lot about the overuse and repetitive motion injuries prevalent in youth sports and the even greater risks with specialization and prodigy sports. One of my favorite points is the importance of "intelligent rest" and the necessity of proper recovery regardless of the sport or intensity. Young growing bodies need to properly recover from these physical demands, particularly with the prodigy sports. Sports medicine and science have come a long way with new methods and tools to help with recovery, but none of them can replace intelligent rest.

Some of the most successful young athletes I've seen over the years in the prodigy sports would take off three-to-four weeks a couple times a year. This means they took a real break from the sport with no training or practice. Physical activities are fine during these breaks such as biking or swimming, but again, no specific sport related activity. Sports parents must insist on these breaks since often the kids or coaches won't!

Another danger is "the mental game" and the real concerns of mental burnout. Sports parents need to be aware that when these prodigy sports kids don't get breaks from their sports, they can lose balance in other areas of their lives. The late sports psychologist, Dr. Jim Vicory, who shared my radio show for a few years in the 1990s, paid special attention to this. He stressed that kids, no matter how serious or talented, need to have fun. They are not small adults but young developing children who need to learn through experience. They are not robots to be consistently drilled.

The pressures, some from sports parents, coaches, and the kids themselves, are very real and relentless. The competition alone can be really challenging. Adding the mental pressures of having to try to play through soreness and overuse and repetitive motion injuries just adds to these problems. We'll hear personally from some sports parents and experts in the last two sections of the book on how best to deal with these questions and challenges.

Hey — whose goal or dream is it? The young athletes or their well-meaning parents?

Fascinating Question!

Some of the pressures to specialize in one sport is often driven by money. Club sports depend on year-round participation at their often expensive facilities and charge a lot of money for specialized training, travel, and equipment. Sports parents too often have "stars in their eyes" and will pay whatever it takes for their child to be successful. Remember that the reality of college scholarships and even professional careers for young athletes is very slim. According to the NCAA, out of the 37 million kids who play organized youth sports, less than 22% of them will play a sport in high school, and out of the 8 million high school athletes, only 2% will play NCAA Division 1 Sports and receive scholarship money, and only 4% of the college athletes will end up playing professionally.[2]

Sports parents need to be very aware of these realities.

ACCORDING TO MY CALCULATIONS, BY REMOVING EVERY OTHER STAIR,
SHE SHOULD HAVE A 40 INCH VERTICAL JUMP BY THE AGE OF SIX.

Chapter 14
Universal Exercises for All Sports

As a sports podiatrist, of course, I'm biased, but the fact is that strengthening your children's feet and ankles is one of the smartest things you can do as a sports parent. So is working balance. It doesn't matter what sport, what level or age. The two very important goals for all parents and coaches is to prevent injuries and when appropriate, enhance performance.

One of the most common of injuries in sports, if not the most common, remains ankle injuries. That alone is a good reason to pay big attention to strengthening them, but that is not the only reason. Strengthening feet and ankles can enhance speed, quickness, agility, and balance — so it's essential in all sports. In all my years seeing many great athletes, I've never seen anyone with "over developed ankles." Weak ankles are usually a link to injuries and a common cause of many sports-related problems.

The body's base and foundation of support are the feet and ankles, but too often they are neglected unless it's rehabilitating a previous injury. It makes much more sense to strengthen and train these areas routinely and proactively.

Old routines usually involved tape or braces for ankles which have a place but are usually for previous injuries or reoccurring problems. These can be helpful but do not replace proper ankle strengthening which is beneficial for all areas above the feet such as the shins, knees, hips, and back. So often we'll see young athletes totally concerned with how much they can bench press or work their arm and shoulder muscles — after all — these are the "show muscles." But these same athletes might have difficulty balancing on one foot! They and their parents and coaches need to be educated about including foot and ankle strength and stability exercises for functional strength- the ability to move with power and speed, change direction, stop and start with balance.

These abilities can successfully be trained with simple, inexpensive equipment such rubber bands and elastic tubing, balance boards, mini trampolines and pieces like the innovative *Sanddune Stepper*. Balance work also enhances and improves knee, hip, core and back stability and strength. Creating imbalance with unstable surfaces demands that all of our stabilizer muscles in our body work to gain and regain stability and balance. I call these exercises "instability training." Try balancing on one foot, or standing on a trampoline or tilt boards. It's challenging, safe and fun! These stabilizers and small muscles help protect all the joints of the feet, ankles, knees, hips and spine. Changing foot positions changes the balance demands to work different areas.

Rubber bands and elastic tubing have always been one of the most effective ways to strengthen all the ranges of motion of our ankles. Moving the ankles up and down, side to side and in and out can strengthen all the lower leg muscles and tendons. Slow deliberate movements are best when using bands or tubing. They are available in different widths and resistance. Have your young athlete start light and move through a full range of motion. Progress gradually.

It is always helpful to get instruction on proper technique and progression from a physical therapist or athletic trainer. These exercises are simple and safe for all ages and levels but don't let their simplicity fool you. Top athletes in all sports have benefited greatly!

Chapter 15
Hey Sports Parents–What About Youth Tackle Football?

It has become one of the great sports debates and dilemmas for sports parents over the past decade. What can be done about the concussions and head trauma in tackle football?

In reality, not much.

The facts are the facts — tackle football is unsafe at any age — period.

Sorry, fans!

We all know in sports medicine the physical orthopedic toll that a collision sport like tackle football involves such as joint, muscle and tendon injuries and the resulting surgeries. Until recently nobody knew the real risk of brain injuries, (all concussions are brain injuries) and the potential of catastrophic consequences. Now that this reality has hit the sport so hard, sports parents are facing the decision of whether to allow their young sons to play tackle football at any age, especially at the young Pop Warner ages that have been commonplace in the past.

I have had many experts on my radio show, from pediatricians, sports doctors, neurologists, neurosurgeons, and psychologists who have been concerned for years. Of course, concussions can happen in all sports and contact is not totally unusual but tackle football is unique in the routine collisions that are a constant part of the game. It's football!

Football is the most popular sport in the USA. The mighty NFL, college football and even high school (Friday Night Lights) are huge. Whole towns live for these games each week. Often their economies depend on them. Big time college programs sure do. Saturdays are filled with wall to wall college games on TV and on Sundays the NFL seemingly replaces religion. The Super Bowl is a national holiday. Young boys have grown up being fans like their dads. Can we expect these young kids to make an informed decision regarding playing football? Obviously not. It's the parent's responsibility to know these very real risks.

For years, ironically, one of football's greatest attractions was "those big hits!" Highlight reels showed the best hits of the game and the more bell ringing, the better. Who knew that those big hits could cause so much trauma to the brain?

The discovery over the past few decades of a serious brain trauma disease C.T.E., (chronic traumatic encephalopathy), has shaken the sport to its core. The recent successful movie "Concussion" brought C.T.E. front and center. This degenerative brain condition is only recognized after death. Almost all former NFL players' brains who have been examined after death have shown the disease. Even some college and high school players' brains that were examined after death showed the disease. C.TE. however, is the horrible endgame because who knows when trouble starts?

The question is:

How many collisions or head hits does it take to cause trouble?

The answer is:

 Nobody knows! It's a crap shoot.

Young players who exhibit headaches, memory problems, sleep problems, and personality changes, among other problems, are far more common than anyone imagined.

Over the past decades, it was thought that helmet technology would solve the concussion challenges. The reality is that helmets, with all their improvements over the years, have protected against skull fractures but not the slamming around of the brain inside the skull which is the real culprit. Besides this fact, these "super helmets-face masks" have become weapons for players who feel virtually indestructible. Watch any game and routinely see headfirst action and players who hit like missiles flying through the air.

Again, the reality is that there is NOT any helmet technology today or in the future that can stop this collision related brain slamming in the skull.

The average high school player probably sustains hundreds of head-related micro trauma per season. Multiply that by five-ten-fifteen seasons! How much is too much? Nobody knows. The powers that be, (and they are powerful), from the mighty NFL on down have been dancing around this forever. Pediatricians and neurologists tell us that the young developing brain is even more susceptible to injury.

My sports medicine colleagues have also been concerned about neck strength lacking in almost all adolescents. It is true that a person can get a concussion falling off a skateboard or bike, sliding into home plate, heading a soccer ball or collision in hockey. But ONLY tackle football is BASED on collision! Hitting the ground is a collision. Blocking and tackling, no matter what the technique, are collisions.

If football is to survive, dramatic changes will have to be made. Tremendous attention has been paid to try and make the sport safer. Rules changes, attention to proper technique and reduced contact and practice time are some examples. Concussion awareness at all levels has increased dramatically. Protocols for the post-concussion return to play rules have improved greatly. There has been an increasing step up in coaching at all levels. In spite of all these efforts, youth participation is going down and sports parents are really backing off.

It's a question for all of us — What will society decide to do with tackle football?

Sports Parents — be educated and pay attention to the real risks of contact sports especially tackle football. Remember that safety should be a number one priority for all sports parents. After all, do we really want to put our child's future health at risk because of a game?

Well, Sports Parents, there you have it. Some very important information regarding key points for prevention and treatment of youth sports injuries, enhancing performance and enjoying and surviving the experience. Hot topics like proper shoes, orthotics, drug and supplement concerns, key exercises, and specialization have all been highlighted.

Here's wishing you the best in navigating this wacky, challenging, world of youth sports.

In the next two sections, we'll check in with some experts and parents for their thoughts and advice on how you and your child can enjoy sports to the fullest!

Dr. Bob

Resources:

1. Reinl, G. (2014) *Iced-The Illusionary Treatment Option.* USA: Gary Reinl. 2nd edition

2. NCAA,D1collegerankings.com

3. LMU Magazine, Winter 2017. Vol 8, No.1 (page 22)

Section Three

THE EXPERTS SPEAK OUT

In the world of youth sports, there are several resources, experts, and doctors available to educate and assist sports parents. In this section, we have assembled some of the most renowned people in the field to contribute their expertise and advice to #HeySportsParents.

The Power Triangle

Robert Andrews, MA, LMFT, Sports Performance consultant, owner of The Institute of Sports Performance, Houston, Texas. Author of Champions Mental Edge, www.tinssp.com

In my work with athletes, I identify what I call the "Power Triangle." This term describes the dynamic relationship between athlete, coach, and parent. Ideally, each component of this triangle, or athlete's system, needs to be strong and open to taking a good hard look at what they can do to make the system stronger. A weakness in any one of these three key components can have a negative impact on peak athletic performance.

Many parents don't realize or fully understand their role in their athlete's training and performance. I am not just talking about paying for lessons or gym fees, car-pooling, or buying equipment. I am also talking about the mental and emotional support they provide or don't provide for their athlete.

Athletes need to be focused on getting better. Their mental and emotional resources play a key role in improving performance. More and more today's athletes are learning how to strengthen their mental approach to their respective sport. They are learning tools, techniques, and concepts to help them be more mindful of their behaviors and emotional responses during performance.

Emotional Intelligence is defined as the ability to manage one's emotions and behavior, and the ability to handle the emotions and behaviors of others. Mindfulness is an awareness of what we are doing when we are doing it. Mindfulness allows us to make non-judgmental observations about our specific mental, emotional, and behavioral responses

Parents who know how to manage their own behaviors and emotions before, during, and after competition can have a huge impact on their athlete's performance, and enjoyment of their respective sport.

Mindful and emotionally intelligent parents are aware of their reactions to bad calls, mistakes, falls, strikeouts, missed free throws, and disastrous performances. These mindful parents are able to step back and internally process what they are experiencing in reaction to their athletes' performance. They take ownership and responsibility for their reactions and behaviors.

Finding Balance

There is a business side and a personal side to a parent's relationship with his or her child/athlete.

The business side is focused on rules, structure, outcomes, scores, placement, commitment, order, improvement, getting that college scholarship, or making a specific team. The personal side is focused on support, emotional connection, passion, engagement, accountability, discipline, and love.

When a parent becomes too focused on either the business side of their relationship with their athlete or the personal side, there can be problems. There will be deficits in the relationship. These deficits between parent and athlete show up as a disconnect, tension, anger, resistance, perfectionism, and passive-aggressive behaviors.

Parents who are overly focused on the business aspect of performance are too locked in on how their athletes perform, how hard they are working, what kind of results they are getting, which team they are playing on, how much playing time they are getting, or if they're starting or sitting the bench. These are parents who always seem to be too intense, too emotional, too involved, or too controlling. They might overstep the boundaries between parent and coach and override a coach's decisions or training methods. They might bring outside support and resources so their athletes will get the training they are certain will get them to the top.

There is not much praise going on in this relationship. This parent doesn't really know how to "fill their athlete's tank" when it comes to emotional support.

These athletes might perform well but are most likely not fully enjoying their involvement in the sport due to their parents' intensity and scrutiny. They usually dread the ride home after a competition because they know they are going to be criticized and drilled for everything they did wrong.

The parent who is out of balance on the personal side of the relationship with their athlete creates deficits in this relationship too. This parent tends to be too lenient, rescues their athlete from struggles, complains about other teammates and coaches in front of their athlete, and helps their athlete shy away from growth opportunities because he or she doesn't want to see their child "suffer." This can cause the athlete to miss out on the many important and powerful life lessons that sports have to offer.

I have two kids that are athletes. My wife and I have had to learn how to sit back and deal with our feelings as we see our kids struggle, suffer from bad coaches, poor teammates, and poor performances. We know that if we move in too quickly, we rob them of the learning opportunities that sports can provide.

We always listen to them and are supportive. We mentor them on how to handle conflict, have a difficult conversation with a coach, deal with a disappointing performance, and take responsibility for their actions and behaviors on and off the field.

Sometimes we have to be strong and tough. Other times we need to be loving and supportive. It is painful to see our kids suffer, but this suffering is often where they acquire the most learning. Learning how to balance our relationships with our athletes makes sports more enjoyable for everyone in the primary triangle.

It frees coaches up to do their jobs and helps hold them accountable when they don't. Athletes train and compete in a supportive environment, and are encouraged to take ownership and responsibility for their actions and performances. Parents have the opportunity to participate and enjoy their athlete's involvement in sports on a much deeper level.

The next time you watch your athlete participate in their sport, mindfully observe yourself. Notice when you get too amped up, too emotional, too angry, or too frustrated. Notice when you want to rush in and deal with a conflict between your athlete and a coach or teammate.

If you do become reactive, step back, take a breath, and see if you can get back to balance mentally and emotionally.

Developing mindfulness and emotional intelligence certainly makes you a better parent to your athlete. The athlete's system will function at a higher level. With a higher functioning system, better performance is certain.

Creating a Solid Fueling Plan at a Young Age
Written by: Kate Davis, MS, RD, CSSD, LDN

Kate is the owner of RDKate Sports Nutrition, a national consulting practice that services athletes as young as 8 and up and at all levels of competition. Kate has previously worked all types of athletes, including young and collegiate, Olympic and professional. She is also a mom and competitive distance runner/triathlete. Check out RDKate.com for more information on her experience, previous clientele, and services — offered remotely and in person.

Elite athletes know that food is not just what they eat. To them, food is what prepares their bodies for performance, sustains them during performance, recovers them after performance and continues that recovery to prevent illness and injury. It also helps muscles better adapt and respond to training.

As a sports dietitian, I have seen young athletes that use food wisely to give them the edge they are looking for. However, I have also seen misuse and misunderstanding of fueling (or complete disregard for it), leading to mental distress and repeat injuries.

Young athletes are in a prime position to be taught the value of a solid fueling plan. This plan should not include crazy dieting, fear of food, or restriction and feelings of guilt. This fueling plan should include a focus on whole foods first while leaving the powders and pills out of the picture. I have taught athletes of all ages how to build a solid fueling program that follows these guidelines.

As a parent, coach or trainer, you can play a key role in supporting a child's positive relationship with food and helping them value food as a tool to their own athletic success. Here are some things you can do:

- First and foremost, remember the roles parents and young athletes have at mealtime. As the parent, you choose what is brought into the house and what your child can choose from at each meal or snack. Your child decides what he/she will eat from what you have offered and also HOW

115

MUCH to eat. So, if all your athlete wants to do is eat three pieces of chicken for dinner and not touch the rest, you should not do or say anything directly to change that. This is a tough relationship for many parents to grasp, but stick with it and check out http://www.ellynsatter-institute.org/ for more reading and resources on the topic.

- Parents, trainers and coaches: be an example of what good fueling looks like. If you don't know what you should be eating, check out mypyramid.gov for a plate visual to get you started. Young athletes model what they see. I have had parents in my office berate their kids for eating poorly while at the same time admitting that they drive their children through greasy burger/fry joints or that they don't stock healthy food options for their kids at home. Whether a child is four or eighteen, they are watching what you do. Be an example to them and they will follow suit.

- Although you may not like or may avoid certain foods, resist making negative comments about food in front of young athletes. Instead, let them form their own opinions about flavor, taste and texture.

- Avoid making comments about how much and what young athletes eat or don't eat. Whether they are the example of perfect eating or couldn't be far enough away, commenting on their eating habits will only teach them to base their worth on food and eating. If you are concerned about an athlete's eating habits, bring them to a sports dietitian (RD, CSSD) who can teach them how to fuel well.

- All food groups play a role in an athlete's fueling pattern. Therefore, except in cases of true food allergies and sensitivities, encourage athletes to eat a variety of whole grains, lean protein, fruits, vegetables and unsaturated fat. Show them that all foods have a place on an athlete's plate (check out the Athlete's Plate visual, among other great resources, at: http://www.teamusa.org/About-the-USOC/Athlete-Development/Sport-Performance/Nutrition/Athlete-Factsheets-and-Resources).

- Encourage young athletes to eat something every two to four hours. Help them choose meals according to the plate visual above and fueling snacks that include a source of protein and either a fruit, grain or vegetable. Eating frequently will assist them with proper growth, recovery and refueling between workouts. Around 30% of high school athletes do not eat breakfast, so parents - don't let them out the door without a solid meal! Athletes often enter practice dehydrated and under-fueled, making snacking before practice imperative; help them get snacks packed so they are prepared.

- For athletes under the age of eighteen, leave supplements out of the picture (except in the case of medically-diagnosed deficiencies as directed by a doctor). The majority of supplements do not work and may contain banned and sometimes dangerous ingredients. Also, athletes risk a positive drug test when taking supplements. Focus on food first with this age group. To have zero risk of a positive drug test, take zero supplements. For more information on this topic, visit NFHS.org.

- Avoid making comments about an athlete's body size or type. Drawing attention to his physical appearance makes him value himself only for how he looks. Making her feel like she is too fat/skinny mistakenly tells her that she would be more competitive or happier if she were different, which isn't always the case. If you have concerns about a child's body, talk (in private) with a doctor or sports dietitian who can evaluate the child and provide him with the correct approach for change – assuming change is necessary. While there are certain body type realities for some sports, there is no one ideal body type for athletes, and trying to fit a "norm" will sometimes make an athlete perform worse — not better.

- Avoid making comments about your own body in front of athletes. Parents: Remember that their bodies are probably just like yours (genetics!). If you insult your body, they might do the same when you aren't around. Imagine that the things you say about your body were being said to your child. How would that make you feel?

- Emphasize positive things about athletes other than appearance. Comments like "I was impressed by your determination out there today," or "Your energy levels looked awesome during practice," will go a long way toward showing them where their worth lies. I'm sure you can think of hundreds of ways your young athletes are awesome, so let them know!

Youth Athletics as Mind Medicine for Life
Dr. Denise McDermott M.D.

As a medical doctor with board certifications in both Adult and Child Psychiatry, she treats children, adolescents, and adults. Her goal is to empower you, your child, and your family to live the best life possible. Her approach is to encourage people to believe in wellness, not illness, and to lead a balanced healthy lifestyle.

www.drdenisemd.com

As an adult and child psychiatrist and as a mom, I believe by encouraging our children to engage in sports we can help set the foundation for overall health, wellbeing and lifelong wellness habits. There is no health without mental health. Regular exercise, good nutrition, and a practice of mindfulness create strong physical and mental wellbeing for all of us and for our children. Let's think of participating in youth athletics as "mind medicine" and lifestyle wellbeing.

We need to pay attention to each child's unique neurostyle (the way they perceive and process the world) and natural athletic inclination to help decide what sport or physical activity matches each individual. One size does not fit all. It is important at a young age that you expose your son or daughter to many different choices: swimming, t-ball, basketball, golf, cheerleading, skating, bowling and more. Try individual and team sports and see what sport activity is the best match for your child. Your child might have sensory challenges, behavioral issues, or physical impairments that warrant patience by you as a parent in helping them to find a realistic athletic activity that they enjoy so they can thrive physically and mentally.

Remember it is not about us living vicariously through our children. We need to respect their growth and development as individuals.

I grew up in the Mid-West playing sports all year round. My parents encouraged me to sign up for all types of sports starting at age four. I excelled at some and others were not my forte. Swimming and soccer were my favorites. My love of the outdoors and swimming landed me a position as a lifeguard and then pool manager. I learned responsibility, discipline, and stayed active at a young age. I also played starting varsity goalie all four years in high school soccer and was asked to play in college. I was fearless as a goalie but after getting kicked in the mouth I realized the importance of protecting my brain. I knew that I wanted to go into medicine and decided that college soccer did not make sense with my professional goals and politely declined an offer to play.

I am sharing this as I think we need to raise our children to be aware of protecting their brain in any contact sport and to teach safe sport practices when encouraging team and individual sports. It is also important for our developing teens entering adulthood to set their own personal athletic, academic and professional goals for their best life.

It is common for parents, young children, and teens to set high expectations and to dream of playing sports in college and beyond. According to NCAA.org "of the nearly 8 million students currently participating in high school athletics in the United States, only 480,000 of them will compete at NCAA schools. And of that group, only a fraction will realize their goal of becoming a professional or Olympic athlete. For the rest, the experiences of college athletics and the life lessons they learn along the way will help them as they pursue careers in other fields. Education is a vital part of the college athletics experience, and student-athletes graduate at higher rates than their peers in the student body."

With this NCAA data in mind, set realistic expectations with your young athlete. A holistic health attitude can be taught at a young age and can last a lifetime. Encourage physical fitness, perseverance, discipline, teamwork, a flexible mindset, good nutrition, sleep habits, and academic excellence. Remind your child that in order to play high school sports, a student-athlete has to maintain a certain grade point average (GPA). This is a fantastic way to link good study habits with the ability to earn and play sports at a young age. A dream of playing professional sports should not be discouraged, yet realistically discussing all of the benefits of playing sports with our children sets a foundation for success in all areas of their life. Participating in individual or team sports should be fun and set an attitude for life success!

Tips to remember:

One size does not fit all. Let your child try different sports that are "a match" for his or her individual needs, skill sets and likes.

Remember it is not about us living vicariously through our children. We need to respect their growth and development as individuals.

As a parent, you are helping your child to create their "Life Mindset" by encouraging perseverance, discipline, teamwork, a flexible mindset, good nutrition, sleep habits, and academic excellence.

Staying active, eating healthy and practicing mindfulness are lifelong "holistic health" attitudes and habits to teach our youth athletes.

Cheers to lifelong health and wellbeing!

Dr. Denise

Concussions and Youth Sports; What Parents Need to Know

By, Dr. Holly Benjamin and Dr. Claire Gross

Holly J. Benjamin, MD, FAAP, FACSM is a Professor of Orthopaedic Surgery, Rehabilitation Medicine & Pediatrics and the Director of Primary Care Sports Medicine at the University of Chicago, a CJSM Associate Editor for CME and the ACSM Vice-President 2016-18

Claire Gross, MD is currently a Primary Care Sports Medicine fellow at Mac-Neal Hospital in Berwyn, IL. She is a member of the American Medical Society for Sports Medicine and serves as a team physician for local high schools.

Everyone these days has heard about concussions due to the tremendous media attention. Fortunately, despite the concerns about brain injury and concussion, we now know more than ever before. Concussions can happen in any sport but are more common in contact or collision sports such as ice hockey, football, and soccer. A lot of research still needs to be done to understand how to prevent and treat concussions.

What is a concussion?

A concussion is a brain injury. It can happen if the head is hit or if a sudden movement makes the brain shake inside the skull.

There are a lot of different symptoms that can be caused by a concussion. Loss of consciousness ("blacking out") can happen, but not often. Possible symptoms from a concussion are:

- Headache
- Head pressure
- Sensitivity to light or sound
- Neck pain
- Nausea/vomiting

- Fatigue
- Trouble with concentration or memory
- Sadness
- Anxiety
- Difficulty sleeping

- Dizziness
- Balance problems
- Difficulty sleeping

- Blurred vision
- Feeling "slow" or "in a fog"

How do I know if my child has a concussion?

A child needs to be able to describe their symptoms in order for a doctor to know that they have a concussion. The doctor will ask the youth athlete questions and do an exam to make sure that s/he did not have any other injuries. If it is determined that the child had a concussion, s/he will not be allowed to play for the rest of the day.

Does my child need a brain scan?

Imaging of the brain with a CT ("cat scan") or MRI ("magnetic resonance imaging") is usually not necessary. However, certain "red flag" symptoms should prompt having the athlete taken to the Emergency Department for further evaluation including brain imaging. These "red flag" symptoms include progressively worsening symptoms listed above, severe headache, one pupil larger than the other, seizures, slurred speech, any abnormalities on a neurological examination, multiple episodes of vomiting, or severely altered thinking (mental status changes).

How is a concussion treated?

Initially, the child needs to rest and avoid intense exercise or thinking tasks. Brain rest, or cognitive rest, means that the child should avoid using computers, video games, phones or any other electronic devices. Resting for a few days will help the athlete feel better faster. Missing a couple days of school is reasonable but every effort should be made to return the child to a "normal" environment as soon as possible, even for partial school attendance. Physical rest from strenuous or high impact activities such as running, jumping or sports is recommended. Physical activity can be slowly reintroduced as tolerated when the child is feeling better.

A very important reference for parents and health care providers comes from the American Academy of Pediatrics (www.aap.org) which has published guidelines for "Return to Learn" and Return to Play" strategies following concussions.

Does my child need to be on medications?

Most children do not need medication to get better from a concussion. Usually, acetaminophen or ibuprofen can help with headaches, and sometimes a doctor may recommend a prescription medication if headaches are severe or to treat other concussion symptoms.

Can other treatments help?

Sometimes, physical therapy might be recommended if a child has lingering symptoms. This treatment might help with dizziness, balance, or vision problems. Psychological therapy can sometimes help with sleep, depression, or anxiety from a concussion and may help with inattentiveness or difficulty understanding schoolwork.

How long do concussions last?

In most cases, concussion symptoms resolve in one to three weeks. If concussion symptoms last longer than expected, usually longer than one month, the child may be diagnosed with Post Concussive Syndrome (PCS). Kids with PCS are more likely to need physical or psychological therapy and/or medications to help recover. Post-concussion syndrome can take weeks to months to recover from.

When can my child return to school?

Children should go back to school gradually after resting. A child may need modifications at school, such as postponing homework or tests, getting notes printed on paper, or even going to school for half-days. A doctor can help decide what accommodations the child needs to succeed at school.

When can my child return to sports?

Once a child's symptoms are getting better, an athletic trainer or doctor can help them gradually increase their physical activity over several days. The athlete should be monitored during this time to make sure the symptoms do not come back. If the symptoms do not return, the athlete will then be allowed to go back to practice, then to games only if they feel 100%. If a child is not attending school full days or has any academic restrictions in place, then he or she is NOT ready to return to any high-risk sports.

Since my child has had a concussion, will they get another one?

If a child has had one concussion, they are at a slightly higher risk to get another concussion in the future, even months or years later. There are no proven ways to guarantee that a child will not get a second concussion. Waiting to return to sports until the child is 100% recovered from the concussion is the best way we know of to decrease the chances of getting another concussion.

Will my child get CTE?

Chronic Traumatic Encephalopathy (CTE) is a disease found in people who have had repeated head trauma. It is rare. It can only be identified at autopsy. It has never been diagnosed in a living person. It has never been diagnosed in a child. At this point, we do not have enough research to be able to predict who will get CTE. In general, it appears that people who get CTE tend to be those with frequent, repeated head trauma, rather than a single concussion. There is a need for more research about CTE.

In Conclusion

Concussions are brain injuries that can have many different symptoms. Some children with concussions will require specific treatments, but the majority of concussions get better with rest. Light physical activity introduced during the recovery period may be helpful but no child can return to a high risk or contact sport until s/he feels 100%. A health care provider such as a physician, nurse practitioner or a certified athletic trainer should determine when it is safe for a child to return to sports.

Behavior of Overzealous Sports Parents on the Sidelines

Ian Goldberg-Founder and CEO of iSports360, Inc.
"Where coaches coach, players play and parents participate"
www.iSport360.com

Concerning the ongoing challenge of the "overzealous" sports parents and their often very questionable behavior, Ian Goldberg, creator of iSport360 has the following insights:

"I've never understood crazy sports parents — what motivates an otherwise law-abiding citizen to act out on the sidelines of a game played by children? What satisfaction do they find hounding coaches for playing time, or harassing referees for perceived mistakes? Do these parents think they're being constructive?" (Jason Gray from the Wall Street Journal article "Let's Put Bad Sports Parents in a Box.")

First, I wholeheartedly agree that we should strongly condemn sideline parents who model poor behavior, poor sportsmanship, a sense of entitlement, and especially those who "chase referees to the parking lot."

That said, at iSports360 we have studied the behavior of sports parents on the sidelines of games with our Board Psychologist Dr. Stephen Feldman Ph.D. According to Dr. Feldman, parents on the sidelines are frequently in "fight or flight" mode, meaning that they have elevated cortisol levels, stress levels, and emotional levels. In fact, many of their actions and words can be defined as "involuntary." This is because they speak/act/yell without applying their normal system of checks and balances.

Additionally, sports parents are spending about 10X what they spent 20 years ago on their kid's sports. So they are, in fact, more demanding of the coaches, trainers, and referees. Not sure whether to blame them or the ballooning youth sports industry for that.

There are nearly 70 million sports parents in our country. Many of them, especially at the more competitive levels, do "hound" their coaches about who gets more playing time, who gets the starting position and who makes the travel team. But to be fair, that is because coaches do not have the time or the tools to share realistic and timely feedback…so parents are frequently in the dark. That is why at iSports360 we created a mobile feedback platform so coaches, parents, and kids can share objective player feedback throughout the season and at try-outs. We've learned a lot about the importance of ongoing feedback from our K-12 Education Advisor Dr. Chris Tienken Ed.D.

Finally, many parents actually DO think they are being constructive and helpful, even when they yell instructions from the sidelines. That's because we spend a fraction of the money educating sports parents than we do educating coaches. Sports parents need to learn that it ruins the youth sports experience when a kid has to decide whether to listen to instructions from their parent or a coach. (And I can't tell you how many times I have counseled young athletes who were dealing with this dilemma). At iSport360 we try to educate sports parents with information and humor and even teach them what is "cheer-worthy" from the sidelines.

While some parents are "yelling, complaining, entitled, know-it-all, rotten, difficult, impossible, and no-good," (to borrow some commonly expressed quotes) most are reasonable people who need a bit of slack and some tools to address their pain points. That is where iSports360 is helping. If you are interested, I'm happy to dig deeper with you on better sports parenting as this topic needs all the attention it can get.

Sincerely,
Ian Goldberg

The Seven Habits Of Savvy Sports Parents

Dr. Dave Epperson, Founder of the Volleyball Festival and member of the American Volleyball Coaches Association Hall of Fame. In 2007, Dr. Epperson was named by the Institute for International Sport as one of America's 100 most influential sports educators.

To help parents prepare themselves for getting and staying connected to their children's experiences in sports, I recommend that they work on developing each of the seven habits of savvy sports parents that I have identified.

www.volleyball-festival.com

Your daughter comes home from softball practice and you ask "How did things go today?" She responds "Oh, OK. I guess." Parents everywhere complain that their teenage children have little interest in talking with them about what goes on at school. Nor do they show much interest in taking advantage of the wisdom their parents have accumulated over the years to help them negotiate their journey through the teenage years. Also, not many children seek their parent's counsel about their lives in sports. Unfortunately, it is often within this cautious, tight-lipped social climate that sports parents have to work with their children to create good sports.

Because this resistance goes with the being a parent of a teenager, you need to avoid beating up on yourself when your children show little or no interest in sharing with you their sports experiences. Does that mean that most children do not want their parents to accompany them on their journey through the world of sports? No, certainly not. Time and again, young people want their parents nearby. But it does mean that children typically want to share their experiences on *their own* terms. They want to dictate what they talk about, when they talk about it, and where they talk about it. Most children do not want to report their failures. They typically do not want to be interrogated before or after a practice or game. And they certainly do not want to answer to you about their sports experiences in front of their peers.

If parents are to inspire their children to share with them their experiences in sports, they need to invest in building the trust that is required for good communication.

When children resist involving their parents in their life in sports it is generally because their history has been dominated by parents who probe, advise, and evaluate. Children do not feel they need any more of these intrusive experiences, especially in relation to an activity that is supposed to be *recreational* and *fun*. For many children, they have concluded that sport is an arena where they do not have to be accountable to their parents. It is enough to be accountable to their coaches and teammates.

To help parents prepare themselves for getting and staying connected to their children's experiences in sports, I recommend that they work on developing each of the seven habits of savvy sports parents that I have identified below. Parents, who have been successful in establishing a collaborative alliance with children in sports typically have developed these habits:

Habit #1   **They Collaborate.**

They establish agreements with your children, their coaches, and the other parents about the role everyone is going to play in the sports communities.

Habit # 2   **They Show Restraint.**

They resist the temptation to intrude into their children's lives in sports.

Habit # 3   **They Support Rather than Promote**

They follow their children's dreams and don't expect the children to follow theirs.

Habit # 4   **They are Enthusiastic, But Mellow.**

They learn to relax and enjoy their children in sports.

Habit # 5   **They Take Advantage of Teachable Moments.**

They develop effective skills for communicating with their children. They avoid monologues.

Habit # 6   **They are Open to Change.**

They are committed to changing their state of mind so that they are able to develop more expansive ways of relating to sports.

Habit # 7   **They Pursue Their Vision of Good Sports.**

They become active leaders for adapting sport to a vision they have developed to guide their actions.

These habits indicate that savvy sports parents are enthusiastic supporters of the cornerstones of good sports.

By reaching agreements with their children about goals and roles, they are showing their children *respect.*

By controlling their responses to rejection and to frustration they are demonstrating *civility.*

By learning to relax and enjoy their children in sports they are communicating to their children that they have *confidence* in their ability to manage their own situations.

By backing off and not intruding into the lives of their children they are allowing their children to take *responsibility* for their own lives.

And by being good citizens in their children's team communities they are modeling responsibility. By investing in preparing their children for being good citizens in their sports programs, and being ready to accept duties in these programs they are reinforcing the importance of establishing a commitment to building a sense of *community* in sports programs for children.

In short, savvy sports parents *are* good sports, they *raise* good sports, and are *collaborators* with athletes, coaches and team parents in creating enriching sports experiences.

Do You Think You Can Help Your Child Become a Better Athlete?

Melissa Orth Fray, a well- respected exercise physiologist, and a single digit handicap golfer, has built her practice around helping others – golfers to business professionals – improve their games, their health and well-being. Melissa coaches a select group of individuals and makes her ideas, health philosophies and best practices available to all through her lecture series, books and videos.

www.corecourage.com

We are all interested in helping to guide and help our children because we love them. One of the most important gifts we can give our children is to teach them to enjoy those things that are healthy for them, like sports.

Oftentimes, what we see today is:

- Depression (2.8 million major depressive episodes/year, ages 12–17)

- Injuries (2.6 million sports-related ER visits per year, ages, 5–24)

- Obesity (12.7 million children, ages 2–19)

- Burnout, early specialization (70–80% attrition rate by age 15)

We want our kids to be confident, competent, and motivated to continue to use their bodies so they stay healthy for life.

Motivation

For children to be 'athletes for life,' they must be self-motivated. This is key for sustained engagement.

Whenever a child does anything, including sports, there are five keys to motivation:

1. Fun

2. Friends

3. Fitting in

4. Mastery, Improvement, and growth (develop physical development)

5. Feeling like they can become good (confidence and psychological development)

Why don't kids do sports?

1. It's not fun

2. Their friends aren't doing it

3. They don't fit in

4. It's past their frustration level

5. They feel they can't ever be good

6. Over-coaching

7. Over-parenting

8. Pain

9. Humiliation

Notice: *The list of why kids don't play sports is twice as long as to why they do.* As parents, we must be aware and mindful. If we optimize the set-up, we support our children much more effectively.

Confidence and Competence

The tools we can use to develop healthy attitudes about exercise and physical health are physical literacy, the five keys to motivation, and long-term athletic development (LTAD).

Physical literacy is cyclical. The child's desire can lead to greater competence that increases confidence which in turn builds more desire.

As parents, we recognize that just as children need to learn the ABCs of reading as an athlete, they also need to learn the ABCs of physical literacy, which are agility, balance, coordination, and speed. Kids need to learn kicking, pushing, pulling, striking, running, skipping, hopping, catching, balance, jumping, visualization, rotating, throwing, integrating core strength, and an awareness of where their body is in space and time, all by the time they are eight or nine years old. These are the building blocks of movement. If we specialize too early in a particular sport, they may learn to run or kick, but not how to throw. We've all heard "You throw like a girl." Unfortunately, many girls are not taught how to throw and catch, which cuts out all sports that use these functional motor movement patterns. They literally have not drawn the blueprint in their brains or in their bodies.

A child who plays many sports develops connections, movement from the core, and strength much more effectively than a child who specializes early. Therefore, the recipe for training a great athlete in one sport is to play many sports through the developing ages and then specialize in a particular sport at the appropriate time, which is around age 16.

Windows of Opportunity/Long-Term Athletic Development

We want, ultimately, for our children to be athletes for life. One framework for achieving this is termed long-term athletic development (LTAD). Studies have shown that LTAD is the optimal way to train our children — and ourselves.

LTAD is a model with developmental windows of opportunity. These ages are approximate, as children develop on a variable timeline.

Window 1: Speed, agility, coordination, balance. Ages 0-8 for girls, 0-9 for boys. Children should be running for 3-5 seconds and then cutting. In this stage, we often mistakenly ask them to run a mile, because we think it's good for them. Instead, short bursts of speed, learning how to balance, and doing things for the first time to develop coordination is most appropriate for this age.

Parents should be loving and supportive, not coaching or demanding. Simply applaud or ask your child how he or she knew how to do a particular activity.

Window 2: Locomotion, stability, object control, awareness. Ages 8-10 for girls, 9-11 for boys. This is the stage where we can give a few instructions on how to develop skills.

Window 3: Learning to play, consolidating sports-specific skills. Ages 11-14 for girls, 12-15 for boys. This is the second window for developing speed. (If we miss either speed window, the child might wind up a race car, but not the rocket ship he or she could have been.) It is also the time when children should still be playing at least two sports. This is one of the most important stages for children because overall risks increase. The National Institutes of Health documents a 70-80% attrition rate for sports participation in this stage, due to injury and/or burnout.

Window 4: Specialization in one sport. Ages 15-21 for girls, 16-23 for boys. This is when children can safely specialize in one sport. When parents hear this, they often gasp because our culture pushes toward specialization much earlier—too early.

As a Parent what can you do now?

It's important to meet our children where they are. If you're wondering what to do now, here are some recommendations:

- Play with your kids.

- Do not worry if you've missed some windows. There are experts who can help bridge the developmental gaps.

- Help your child frame their activity like an athlete. Athletes fuel, train, and rest. They don't 'diet and exercise. '

- Continue to pay attention. Know that it is never too late to start.

If you are reading this, you yourself are most likely in the final window of opportunity. That's okay! We want athletes building athletes. Understand that movement is a way of life. Keep learning and building your own skills. Continue moving with your friends, having fun, fitting into the activities you enjoy, feeling that you can grow and develop. If we model movement as fun and connected to people we love, we will help our children's confidence, competence, and motivation not just in sports, but throughout life.

What Great Sports Parents DO

Janis B. Meredith, certified life coach for sports parenting, owner of a youth sports parents blog jbmthinks.com.

As a sports mom for 22 years and a coach's wife for 29, I know both sides of the bench in youth sports. I've seen the value of all that youth sports can teach kids. My own kids are now 24,27, and 30, and I know that a big part of who they are is because of the years of sports they played — from preschool through college.

Because I believe so strongly in the value of youth sports, I want to help busy and often overwhelmed sports parents by providing guidance and resources to guide them as they strive to give their children a growing and positive youth sports experience.

I talk about hundreds of topics on my blog, such as dealing with difficult coaches, playing time issues, motivating athletes and teaching good sportsmanship.

I want to help parents guide their children to get the most of their sports experience. Sports should be more than just a game — more than wins and losses, more than stats and scholarships. Competition provides a perfect setting for character growth. I've seen just about everything in youth sports — good and bad. And I feel strongly about helping parents and young athletes build character through the athletic experience.

Playing sports brings excitement and recognition. It may even help pay for college and open doors for the future. But nothing will ever be more important than the type of person your son or daughter becomes in the process.

Here are a few of the reasons why your sacrifice as a sports parent is worth it. Youth sports helps kids:

- perform better in the classroom while developing greater personal confidence and self-esteem

- establish stronger peer relationships

- show more restraint in avoiding risky behavior

- make friends including those of different races

- develop greater family attachment and more frequent interactions with parents

- experience better moods and alleviates many forms of depression

- be less likely to be overweight or obese, depressed, smoke, use illicit drugs, or have unwanted teen pregnancies

- learn emotional control

- learn the value of teamwork show initiative

- start a lifelong habit of staying active

Here are a few things great sports parents do:

- They know that youth sports should be fun and they let themselves enjoy it.

- They enjoy the journey and look for the little victories.

- They know that mistakes are for learning and they give their kids permission to fail.

- They know that success is not given, it's earned and they let their kids do the hard work.

- They understand that it takes a team, and they model that to their kids by doing their part to help.

- They recognize the futility of pushing too hard and instead opt to do more listening and asking.

- 7. They believe that the bigger picture of youth sports is paramount and they let that drive every sports parenting decision.

If you believe that youth sports are not all about wins, stats, and college scholarships, that it is an opportunity for your child to learn key lessons that will stay with him for life, then you have bought into the philosophy that the bigger picture of youth sports is what's important. That belief should drive every sports parenting decision you make.

Let's be honest, the chances are slim that your child is going to get a full ride scholarship to college and end up in the pros. If you are counting on that and in the process ignoring all the amazing opportunities to help your child learn huge life-impacting lessons, you have missed out on a gold mine.

Youth Sports Safety

Dr. Steve Horwitz, was selected by the United States Olympic Committee as the sole chiropractor for the 1996 United States Olympic Team and has traveled internationally with U.S.A. Track and Field. He is the chairman of the USA Track and Field Potomac Valley Sports Medicine Committee and the Maryland Chiropractic Association Sports Council. He was the team chiropractor for George Mason University, has worked with athletes from Georgetown University and University of Maryland and currently consults with American University. He treats athletes from many local high schools as well.
www.teamsafesports.com

The Good News: "I've been an expert witness on 35 cases where deaths have happened in sport ... and in almost all the cases, the death was preventable with relatively simple, simple policies and procedures." [1]
Doug Casa, Korey Stringer Institute

"An ounce of prevention is worth a pound of cure."
Benjamin Franklin

Would we drop our children off at a pool without a lifeguard?

Of course, the answer is "no." Yet, we do drop off our kids at sports games and practices. Do we have the knowledge that the coaches are trained and that the sports organizations are prepared?

The National Athletic Trainers Association reported that 37% of U.S. public high schools and 18% of private high schools have at least one full- time Athletic Trainer (AT).* [2][3]

*NOTE: An Athletic Trainer is not the same as a Fitness Trainer. Athletic training requires a minimum of a baccalaureate degree and more than 70 percent of athletic trainers hold at least a master's degree. Education includes acute injury care, orthopedic and medical diagnoses, pharmacology, psychology, and nutrition. [4]

At the middle school level, AT coverage is usually limited to football and in youth sports "such as Little League, Pop Warner, and CYO, and athletic trainers are essentially non-existent."[5]

Since sports injuries are part of the game, what can be done to mitigate injury risk?

1. Rules Changes.

   In youth ice hockey, removing body checking from youth under age 13 lead to a leads to a "67% reduced risk of concussion in 11-year-old and 12-year-old hockey players."[6] In US Soccer eliminated heading soccer balls for youth players younger than 10 years and limited the practice of heading for children ages 11 to 13 years. In youth football changes are currently being made like smaller fields, no 3 point stance, making sure players are of equal size and fewer players on each team.[7] Talk to your organization about ways to remove or limit collisions.

2. Equipment and Surfaces

   a. **Player Equipment:** Make sure your child has the correct equipment and that it fits properly. Helmets, body pads, shin guards all require proper fitting. Follow the manufacturer's instructions. In addition, a proper mouth guard is essential. On a national level, all states generally mandate mouth guard use in high school football, ice hockey, men's lacrosse, field hockey, and amateur boxing.[8] Proper eyewear and footwear are also important. Keeping uniforms and equipment clean and self-cleanliness is critical to preventing the spread of infectious disease.[9]

   b. **Field and court Equipment:** Soccer, lacrosse, and ice/field hockey goals must be anchored properly and the nets properly secured.[10]

It is the same for basketball nets. Fields and courts should be inspected for cracks and holes.

3. Ask questions

    a. **Who comprises the organization's sports medicine team?** Someone has to know when to remove the child from play, someone has to know when the child can return to play, and someone has to have oversight over safety policies and procedures.

    b. **Emergency Action Plan (EAP):** Does the organization have an EAP? Is it posted? Where?

        i.   Who is responsible for on-field care?

        ii. Who calls 9-1-1?

        iii. Who takes care of the rest of the team and manages the spectators?

        iv. Who meets the ambulance?

        v.   Who travels with the athlete?

        vi. Is there an AED and first aid kit available?

        vii. Who notifies emergency contacts and documents the incident?

    c. **Preparticipation Physical Examination**

        i.   Has the athlete had a thorough preparticipation physical examination and Is it documented?[11]

d. Emergency Contact and Emergency Medical Information

    i. Are these immediately available to the coach?

    ii. Can this medical information be easily updated and communicated?

    iii. If a medication is necessary for an emergency (EpiPen®, asthma inhaler), is it immediately available to your child? In other words, will you be present at every game and practice with medication in hand or will you discuss a plan with the coach and allow him/her to carry and/or administer the medication if you are not present?

    iv. If the child is young (under 13), consider giving the coach consent to carry/administer this medication in an emergency if you cannot attend.

    v. And to the administrators — is this consent documented?

e. Coach Education

    i. Is there a requirement for the coaches to be educated on all potential issues including concussions, heat, and sudden cardiac arrest, anaphylaxis (EpiPen® use), allergies (inhaler use), infections (MRSA), bleeding, fractures, seizures, etc.? Is this documented?

    ii. Is there a requirement for parents to be educated? Is this documented?

f. Heat Plan

i. Does the organization have a heat plan based on the heat index at the practice/game location? Mandatory water break intervals and rest periods. Vigilant monitoring of athletes and heat index.

- GREEN FLAG <95°F

- YELLOW FLAG 95°F – 99°F Activities capped at 2.5 hours

- RED FLAG 100°F – 105°F Activities capped at 2 hours

- BLACK FLAG >105°F Outdoor activities forbidden

ii. Are ice baths made available at every practice and game?

iii. Is a shaded area made available at every practice and every game

iv. Are the athletes being weighed twice every day, before and after practice/games? > 3% weight loss as compared to prior day – indicates that they should not participate in physical activities

g. Concussion Management System

i. Who removes the player? Parent, coach, referee?

ii. Who documents the signs and symptoms (triggers)? What are those signs and symptoms? Does everyone know these?

iii. Who is notified? When and how? Phone, fax, email, SMS, FB message, Skype, Facetime?

iv. What is the return to play protocol?

v. Where is the doctor's note?

vi. To whom is it given? Where is it stored?

vii. Is the doctor familiar with the latest concussion guidelines?[12]

viii. What is the date of return?[13]

ix. Who monitors/tracks/documents each step of the protocol?

x. How is each step during this process communicated? To whom?

For More Information and a Complete Safety Plan Go to TeamSafe™
www.TeamSafeSports.com

We enroll our kids in organized sports because of the many benefits to be gained. And we just love to watch them play! Yet, with any physical activity, especially in sports, there is the risk of physical injury. We know that the decisions made in the first minutes after an injury will significantly influence the ultimate outcome. As attorney Al Goldberger has said, "Somebody has to know when to have the child taken out and evaluated or the whole thing breaks down."

With some simple steps as outlined above we can dramatically reduce the risk of injury and improve the outcome should an injury occur. With the proper systems in place, parents will have peace of mind, coaches will have the education and training they deserve, and administrators will have a risk mitigation strategy for the organization. And most importantly, our kids will be that much safer.

[1]https://ksi.uconn.edu/tag/policies/

[2]http://natajournals.org/doi/pdf/10.4085/1062-6050-50.2.03?code=nata-site

[3]http://natajournals.org/doi/pdf/10.4085/1062-6050-51.11.04?code=nata-site

[4]https://www.nata.org/about/athletic-training/education-overview

[5]http://www.nwitimes.com/sports/columnists/john-doherty/john-doherty-with-going-on-who-will-take-care-of/article_18d96b19-5b12-57ca-b953-ad-123437cdf0.html

[6]https://www.ncbi.nlm.nih.gov/pubmed/28254746

[7]https://www.npr.org/sections/thetwo-way/2017/02/01/512835175/big-rule-changes-could-make-youth-football-games-a-whole-lot-smaller

[8]http://www.academyforsportsdentistry.org/faq-s#What_states_mandate_mouth-guards

[9]http://pediatrics.aappublications.org/content/early/2017/09/21/peds.2017-2477

[10]http://anchoredforsafety.org/

[11]https://www.aap.org/en-us/about-the-aap/Committees-Councils-Sections/Council-on-sports-medicine-and-fitness/Documents/PPE-4-forms.pdf

[12]http://bjsm.bmj.com/content/51/11/838

[13]https://www.teamsafesports.com/possible-concussion

Section Four
PARENT PERSPECTIVES

Dr. Weil rounded up a group of sports parents who spent years guiding their children through the rigors, challenges, and joys of youth sports and asked them to share their experiences. Topics include the goals they set for their athletes, some of the challenges and highlights, and their advice for other sports parents. After reading their stories, you will realize what it takes on the part of the athletes and their parents to accomplish the dream of making it to the top of a sport.

Kirk Mango, author of Becoming a True champion, former NCAA gymnastics champion, dad of two Division 1 volleyball and soccer players

As parents, probably the most important goals for us was to work toward raising daughters who are independent, self-sufficient, and responsible people willing to take personal ownership of whatever it is they seek to achieve or want out of life. We tried to teach them that when things don't go their way, how important it is to look in the mirror FIRST for THE answer or solution...inside oneself rather than outside. We also wanted them to realize that no matter what cards they had been dealt or circumstances they face, that they are personally responsible for seeking to take control over their own destiny. Blaming others was not an option. And lastly, we wanted to teach them how important it is to stay focused on the "PROCESS" rather than on any outcome they seek because it is this process type thinking that is transferable to any area of life. Outcomes are simply possibilities that happen based on this process.

It is to this end, above, that competitive sports held the utmost importance, as it is here where the intrinsic value of athletic endeavor holds its greatest impact. This held especially true for both our daughters. Our oldest struggled through surgery/rehab for a torn ACL one year, and further surgery/rehab to repair complete ligament tears of her ankle two years later to play DI soccer (on scholarship). Our youngest battled against the "you're too short" perspective (at 5'4") in volleyball to become "player of the year" in Illinois, securing All-American at club volleyball nationals and a scholarship to play DI volleyball.

Aside from the adversity mentioned above, the biggest challenge for us as parents centered on keeping our kids from falling into the norm of the "short-term gratification" thought process that many young people in our society have embraced. However, competitive sports can help greatly in this challenge as it can be an opposing force against the pressures our youth are bombarded by on a daily basis as long as the focus is centered in the "right" areas and life lessons are emphasized as part of this focus.

The highlights of being a sports parent included the accomplishment of the goals and objectives sought by both girls...regardless of the adversity they faced. There is no thrill greater than to witness one's own offspring face such difficulty head on, stand strong against it, and accomplish what they set out to do.

Secondly, and most importantly, it was incredibly gratifying to see how well both girls have taken the principles learned through their athletic experiences and applied those same principles to successes in life, thus, demonstrating how the true intrinsic value of competitive sports participation extends well beyond the athletic arena.

Some of the specific highlights include watching our oldest daughter come back from the two serious injuries mentioned earlier, and return to competitive form, as well as compete for a top level DI college soccer program, Marquette University. Our youngest daughter, who was told she was too short to play volleyball, went on to help her high school team win their first state volleyball state championship as their starting libero. The look on her face, after the last point, was and still is, unforgettable. A close second would be her selection as the libero and captain of her club volleyball team that went on to win both USAV and AAU National Championships as well as her selection as captain of her Louisville University volleyball team in her senior year.

What advice would we give to other sports parents? First, give solid and sound thought to the principles you, as parents believe in, and hold to those principles when raising your kids while keeping in mind the importance of being flexible. There are few absolutes in life and being flexible based on circumstance will be an essential ingredient in raising healthy, well-adjusted kids as long as that flexibility doesn't put at risk the foundations you are trying to build within your offspring through the principles you believe are essential.

Secondly, always keep in mind that success in competitive sports, or in anything, MUST come from within. This is especially true with kids, as it is essential to remember that it needs to be about them…it is THEIR story that THEY must write, as well as decide how that story will be written.

Cat Dols, second mom of Brant Moles, 1997 World Extreme Ski Champion, speaker, life coach and author of *Get Your Goddess On, Own Your Power, Love Your Life.*

When a child makes the commitment to become an athlete, we as parents, become part of the team and shift into a new mindset. For me, my son's sport was skiing. He started at a very young age on a tiny ski hill in the Midwest and eventually won the 1997 World Extreme Ski Championship in Alaska.

Our journey was filled with understanding, support and continuous belief in his abilities to make it to the Olympic Ski Team. Of course, there were also countless sacrifices made for training, race schedules and a ski academy for High School. GMVS was so dedicated to the training schedules of their students that the class schedule was regularly rearranged because of the daily snow conditions.

The biggest challenges that effected Brant's dreams were the many injuries he incurred along the way. The largest one being his $35,000 thigh, when he shattered his femur and was airlifted off the hill in severe shock. At that time, he was training to be on the Olympic Ski Team. With a rod and pins anchoring his bones, he continued to ski like a mad man and at one time, jokingly asked for another rod and pins set up in the other leg, so he could be invincible! Did I also mention that patience and a sense of humor are also part of being an athlete's parent?

After he healed, he was beating some of the members of the US Ski Team, but was turned down and told he was too old to be on the team at 24! As a parent, the best place I could go to after his dreams were shattered, was just to listen and be the sounding board he needed to create a new dream.

And then along came *extreme skiing*, which involves jumping from high cliffs and down steep slopes…something that he already loved to do. He excelled, and within a couple of years, he was the World Champion! It gave him great pleasure and me lots of grey hair. The very best way for me to support him was to continue to believe in him every step of the way.

Today Brant coaches older kids and adults, using techniques to improve their skiing and helping to alter their mindset after injuries. He also travels the world, judges racing and extreme competitions, has been in countless ski movies and is presently in the process of writing a book. I am extremely proud of the difference he has made in the skiing world.

All the sacrifices, grey hair and long hours were worth it to see him achieve his dream, as he inspired many others in the process with some even calling him their idol! My best advice to parents of athletes: if someone tells your children they can't, start the conversation as to why they CAN, simply by making new choices. Help them to clear out the doubts, encourage healthy self-talk and listen to their desires. It's the best gift you can give them in the end.

Nancy Ryan, parent of Chloe Ryan, USFSA 2017 National Solo Dance Champion, Junior Combined, and 2017 National Solo Dance Champion, Pre-Gold Pattern Dances

In September 2017, our fifteen-year-old daughter became a two-time USFSA National Champion. As this achievement was the culmination of ten years of specialized training, I have been asked what it is that most helps a young elite athlete to succeed. What is it that sets the athlete apart from others and allows the athlete to become 'the best' or "first' or a champion?

The regimen for an elite athlete is grueling and, in our daughter's case, year-round. Throughout the past decade, numerous challenges were faced. She was constantly bruised and battered from falls. Sometimes it was coaches, and sometimes she just pushed herself beyond reason. Regardless, she experienced countless injuries: recurring plantar fasciitis, a fractured wrist, concussion, stress fracture in her back, sprained foot and ankles, hip and knee injuries, pinched nerves, fractured knee. The first of these (plantar fasciitis - in both feet) appeared one year into her skating career. In order to continue skating, her podiatrist (Dr. Weil) made custom orthotics to fit into her skates. She decided to stop formal ballet training. It was the first of dozens of times that she would choose skating over all else.

Injuries kept her from doing what she loved most. Each time she was away from training, she spent weeks in physical therapy. Seeing others continue on and realizing there may be a lot of catching up was overwhelming. Both physical rehabilitation and the psychology of 'starting over' needed to be addressed time after time. She needed help physically and mentally for re-entry into skating.

Another challenge she faced was feeling different from non-skating friends and not fitting in because of her skating. Sleep and dietary habits set her apart. She ate healthy food when no one else did. She went to bed and got up very early for lessons and training. She missed other experiences and activities. Skating brought her attention and other friends and parents were sometimes envious of that. They didn't understand her dedication, commitment, and passion for excellence. That lack of understanding sometimes left her feeling isolated or different.

As parents, our goals included juggling the schedule, funding the sport (equipment, specialty trainers, costumes and dresses, travel expenses for competitions), helping her to fit in with others were are not on an elite sport track, working with school officials for special consideration, making travel arrangements and providing the best environment possible. The following keys played a primary role: patience and understanding, willingness to listen, being a sounding board, providing encouragement, and running interference when needed. Being able to recognize that the intensity of training can lead to burnout is critical to the athlete's success. Stepping in when the athlete needs to find balance and providing the opportunity to regroup and decompress is essential in order to refocus on priorities. On one occasion, we arranged a last minute weekend trip to the Grand Canyon for this very reason. But perhaps the most critical key was to allow her voice to be heard and to then advocate in whatever ways were necessary to help her exert control and reach her goals in skating.

A 'normal' life will be difficult for the elite athlete. Physical challenges and human challenges (people that may try to bring them down) will be rampant. With social media playing a major role in peoples' lives, it's mandatory to have a large cheering squad for the athlete. We couldn't do this alone. It literally took a village, a strong team of experts to support her throughout her journey. We found and recruited many strong, supportive adult team players. These people always propped her up. Her team of support had a rotating cast of characters including a strong unit of various skating coaches, specialty dance and acting instructors, strength trainers, mental coaching, and highly specialized medical support in the form of a podiatrist, physical therapist, acupuncturist, physiatrist, homeopathic physician, and dietician. Each of these contributed specialized skills to the team, all with the goal of building and supporting our skater.

In our case, our daughter had an exceptional skill set that allowed her to grow and become a champion ice dancer. Her resilience to the challenges and obstacles laid before her was built on the foundation provided by the many, many supporters on her 'team.' Her road to becoming a champion was long and arduous, but with help from her support system, she navigated the many bumps successfully. With their help, her goal to become a champion was fulfilled. Yet, the best reward of all was the happiness at reaching the mountaintop after the long, long climb.

Athletes Journey
Timmer Halligan, youth tennis coach to young champions and dad of two highly ranked tennis daughters

For nearly 30 years I have been coaching athletes, parenting athletes and coaching parents to be the best parents they can be for their athletes. I have been blessed to help 70 plus tennis players receive Division 1 scholarships, earn millions on the professional tour, help countless become successful business owners, doctors, lawyers, actors, and coaches of the great game I taught them. But, I have also seen many that have quit the game of tennis and have had relationships with parents strained. The sad part is that the parents truly want what's best for their child, but through an improper understanding of their role and the ability to communicate it effectively, they actually stunt their child's growth in the sport or activity they participate in. Believe me when I say that I have messed this up a few times with my own children, but what I have learned over the years is that if you want to have your children be champion athletes, we have to be champion parents. It's all the same mindset.

Over the years, as a coach, my intentional philosophies have changed. I can remember in the early 90's while in my early 20's I thought coaching was about the winning, the thrill of victory, winning the championships, never intentionally realizing that what led to their success was always putting the child first. It was always about making the child the best version of themselves that they could be. Ironically, as I have been writing this article over the last couple of months, many of the athletes that I coached in my early years have come back to me and shared what an impact I made in their lives and what a tremendous influence I was to them. My initial thought was, I wish I would have the experience and technical skills I have today and I could have made them a much better player, but then I realized I gave them the greatest skill that you can give a child which is the belief that they can accomplish anything if they set their mind to it.

What I lacked in skill and experience I made up for in positive reinforcement and enthusiasm. So what does this have to do with parenting an athlete? Everything!

Fast forward to 2004 when my son started to compete, and I became that "Tennis Parent." My cool, calm, sideline demeanor when my athletes were competing turned to stress, frustration, and even anger when my son didn't perform his best. Can you relate? All those things I tell parents never to say, I found myself saying to my own child. "Do you know how much this is costing me?" "Why can't you give your best, every time you are on the court?" "The other players are going to pass you up as they work harder."

And then it hit me like a ton of bricks! I said these things because I loved him with all my heart and soul and wanted what was best for him. However, I was too emotionally tied to the outcome. My intentions were good, but my delivery and message came out like Edward Scissorhands trying to comb his hair. It was not a pretty sight. As a result, he stopped enjoying the game, didn't learn the lessons that might have been learned from playing the sport and ultimately quit. For that, I will always have regrets and for parents reading this passage today you have the opportunity to make your child's athletic experience the best that you can.

Fast forward to 2017. I have two daughters, ages 13 and 11 playing tennis across the country and their experience is much different from my son's because I have learned to emotionally detach from the wins and the losses. Yes, I still coach them with others help of course because I am still "dad" but I have learned to appreciate every good and bad shot because they are part of their getting better.

I have always said let the players play, let the coaches coach and let the parents parent. These roles are tough to adhere to but, when you can remind yourself to adhere to these philosophies, your family's journey in athletics will be a more pleasurable one.

This doesn't mean you can't be sad or frustrated when your athlete has a tough day on the courts. We are human, *but it does mean we should not show it*. That's the champion mindset, as nothing good can come from it. When your child finishes that tough match, suffers a tough loss, makes some poor choices with their behavior, they need you more as a parent than anything else. First give them about 15-30 minutes of space after the game, as they are most fragile at that moment. Personally, I would just give them a hug and say "I love you." But later, they need you to tell them "there will be another match." "today may not have been your best day," "did you feel your attitude was the best it could have been?" "did you feel you prepared as well as you could have?" Most importantly you must tell your child that you love him or her and that today was all part of the journey. This is so much easier to read and agree than to do. These approaches create a positive, caring and learning experience like no other for your child.

They key thing to remember is to refrain from lecturing and let your child answer the questions freely without judgment which will open the door for more communication. The best response always is that "you can work on that with your coach." The second best response is: "Do you want to get some ice cream?"

As a former professional athlete, parent, and coach I have seen all sides of the equation and as I stated at the beginning. So if you want to have your child be a champion in life, we must be champion parents. It's all the same mindset.

Sharkie Zartman, a former national team volleyball athlete and mother
of two NCAA Division 1 volleyball players

As a mom of two daughters who played volleyball, I know the road to success for both young athletes and their parents is very challenging, but also fulfilling. As a former USA National Team athlete and All-American in the sport, I remember feeling both excited and also hesitant when my girls said they wanted to play volleyball. I knew the hardships and struggles I had endured to get to the top and wasn't so sure I wanted to see my daughters go through them. They were also very young when my husband and I started a club for kids their age. Our goals at the time were for all the kids to learn the footwork and skills correctly and also to have fun, and to be able to make their school teams if desired. My daughters also did other sports and loved being active, competing, and making new friends.

As far as my daughters' goals were concerned, they both just really wanted to play their best and help their teams win. They never really had any intentions to play at a high level until they went to high school and started playing doubles on the beach and began winning championships. However, college scholarships at the time seemed to be almost unattainable because they were both "vertically challenged." Teri was 5'5," and Chrissie was 5'2", both supposedly too short to play at that level.

Some of the challenges as parents included the helpless feeling of not being able to help our daughters achieve a goal because of their size. Both of my daughters wanted to play in college, and I remember feeling upset that they were doomed because their dad and I were not tall. Both girls had skills, determination, and knew how to win, however, some of the college coaches were not interested in them because of their height.

I think one of the highlights of our journey was at one of the National Junior Events when our club team played against a team that had the tallest athletes in the tournament. The stands were full of college coaches because they were going after these prized athletes. I remember when my team went out on the court, the "tall team" started laughing at us. All of their players were well over six feet tall, and our team averaged 5'6." But, skills and determination are huge advantages, and unfortunately for the other team, those were not their strengths.

We won the match easily, and I think taught everyone a lesson including the coaches. And yes, my daughters both got full scholarships, one to UCI and the other to UCLA. In addition, my younger daughter was named as a Division 1 All-American her senior year in college.

As a mom, I know what it feels like to watch your kids play sports. At times I felt euphoric and proud, other times angry, sad or just frustrated. I think this is all normal now as I look back. Being both a mom and a coach, I know that there are many things you cannot control, but you can always support and be there for your child. You cannot play for them. So as a sports parent, get ready for a wild ride. There will be ups and downs for sure. And when it is over, you will hopefully be able to look back and have some fantastic memories. And even if they don't get a scholarship, play professionally, or win a championship, the time spent being there for your child will be precious. You will be amazed at what they are capable of and how they grew so much by playing sports.

A Final Word

Sports parenting is one of the hardest jobs you'll ever love. It's similar to riding a roller coaster with its ups and downs and twists and turns. It will be exhilarating, challenging, fun, stressful, and at times scary.

Talk about a wild ride!

Are you ready?

Hopefully, your experience will be positive for you and your child. No one can promise success, fame, or a full scholarship. But what I can guarantee, is that if you have the right perspective and can help your child through the maze of youth sports, the time spent will be cherished no matter what happens regarding wins, losses, scholarships or professional opportunities. The medals, trophies, and certificates eventually fade, but the memories will live on and become more valuable as you age.

Picture yourself sitting across the table from your child twenty years from now. He or she is an adult and probably has a life filled with responsibilities and most likely will no longer be competing in a sport. When you and your child reminisce about the early sporting days, will the conversation be lively, fun and filled with stories? Will your child tell you about the lessons he or she learned while playing sports, the fond memories of the teammates and coaches, and thank you for being there during the journey? Or will it be a negative discussion about how horrible the experience was and how much they hated the sport?

As I look back on our parenting years with our daughters in sports, I can tell you that all the worries and problems we took so seriously back then are now distant memories. Even though they were both successful in their sport, they don't talk about the wins or losses. They talk about the fun times, crazy stories, and all the people they met during those years. I feel so blessed to have been there for that part of their experience in life, and now see how much they have grown and utilized the lessons learned from being an athlete.

But I'm not done yet.

My five–year-old grandson, Calvin, just started playing youth sports this year (soccer and baseball). I can see where this is going to be quite an escapade for him and his parents. And then there is my granddaughter, Clara, who is two-years-old, and is already talking about becoming an Olympic skater.

As their grandmother, (ZMA), I feel that I have an advantage over my kids since I already went through the journey with them as a parent/coach.

However, as I watch my little grandson step on to the field, everything feels new again. I experience the exhilaration and anticipation all over again. However, this time, it's not as intense as it was when I was a young parent. I hope he has a great ride playing sports and learns all he can from them. I know that I did, and so did my daughters.

In closing, Dr. Bob and I wish you the best! We hope that you enjoyed the book and learned some valuable sports parenting tips. Our intention for putting this book together was so that all sports parents and their children would be able to enjoy sports to the fullest and reap all the benefits they have to offer.

Enjoy the journey!

About the Authors

Sharkie Zartman, MS, professor, author, coach, speaker, radio host

Sharkie Zartman is a USVBA five-time All-American volleyball athlete and champion competitor at UCLA where her jersey was retired. She was a member of the U.S. Women's National Volleyball Team and also competed in the Women's Professional Volleyball Association for five years and is a member of the California Beach Volleyball Hall of Fame.

As a coach, Sharkie led El Camino College to nine league and two state titles, and with her husband, Pat, she helped the South Bay Spoilers club team win multiple national titles.

Sharkie holds degrees in kinesiology and instructional technology. She teaches health and fitness at the community college and hosts "Sharkie's Pep Talk" on Healthy Life Radio. Sharkie is a certified health coach with the official sanction of the New York State Education Department and the Institute of Integrative Nutrition. She is also a dynamic speaker and is passionate about inspiring people to live their best life at any age.

Sharkie has authored six books, including:

Have Fun Getting Fit; Simple Ways to Rejuvenate Your Mind and Body
Take on Aging as a Sport; The Athletic Approach to Aging
Shark Sense; Getting in Touch with Your Inner Shark
So You Think You Can Coach Kids?
Youth Volleyball; The Guide for Coaches and Parents
Empowered Aging; Expert Advice on Staying Healthy, Vital, and Active

Website: www.sharkiezartman.com

Dr. Robert A. Weil, the Sports Doctor ™

Dr. Robert A. Weil, Sports Podiatrist. Dr. Bob has treated many of the world's premier athletes from all types of sports. He is the host of "The Sports Doctor™" Radio Show. The show is now featured on BBS Radio Network & Sports 4 Fanz Radio. Dr. Bob was formerly on HealthyLife.net Radio and also on WDCB public radio in Chicago for over twenty years. He has written articles for many newspapers and magazines and is a frequent guest on other networks.

Dr. Bob's articles and past shows are available on his website:
http://sportsdoctorradio.com

"The Sports Doctor™" radio show network is growing. We are now on BBS Radio Networks numerous stations live streaming on Wednesdays at 3pm CST. Tune-In at https://bbsradio.com/thesportsdoctor. The show is also available at BBS radio as a podcast.

Join the Sports Doctor and his great guests for important topical information for injury free exercise, wellness and Sports Performance for both adults and kids.

Made in the
USA
Monee, IL